6-25-70

★

Full Hold and Splendid Passage *tells about America at sea (merchant marine, not navy) from 1815 to 1860, through the journals and recollections of the men who sailed the ships. It is a personal documentary portrait of sea life, answering questions of interest to young people such as: What was it really like? What did the sailors eat? What were their moods, their relationships with one another, with the officers, the cook, the people they met in foreign lands? What was their attitude toward authority? How did it feel to struggle with storm-whipped canvas 160 feet above the deck in the face of driving sleet and snow? From their commentary evolves a living picture of the development of the transatlantic packet trade, the China trade, the California gold rush, whaling, and the brutal business of running slaves.*

The Living History Library is a new series, under the general editorship of John Anthony Scott, that provides a fresh, challenging, and human approach to the study of the American past. Its overall theme as a series is the history of the United States as told by the people who shaped it. In each book, songs, documents, letters, and diaries are joined by a sustaining commentary to illuminate a given facet or topic in the history of the American people.

FULL HOLD AND SPLENDID PASSAGE

The Living History Library

General editor: John Anthony Scott

FULL HOLD AND SPLENDID PASSAGE

AMERICA GOES TO SEA

★ *1815 - 1860* ★

Bill and Gene Bonyun

With maps, contemporary prints, and songs

ALFRED A. KNOPF : NEW YORK

Acknowledgment is gratefully made to Houghton Mifflin Company for permission to
reprint from One Whaling Family, edited by Harold Williams; and to The Macmillan
Company to reprint "Paddy Get Back" from Shanty Men and Shanty Boys,
by W. M. Doerflinger, Copyright 1951 by W. M. Doerflinger.

1536239

CONTENTS

★

FULL HOLD AND SPLENDID PASSAGE

SEA HERITAGE

Like an eagle caged I pine
On this dull, unchanging shore;
O give me the flashing brine,
The spray and the tempest's roar.

"A Life on the Ocean Wave"

Adventure at sea has always been one of the great dreams of the American boy. If he happened to live near the Atlantic coast during the first half of the nineteenth century, realization of the dream was very possible indeed, and in thousands of young hearts it grew to a passion that could only be satisfied by fulfillment. For some the reality was more than enough: the hardships of a single voyage sent them scurrying back to shore again. But for others the only cure was a lifetime at sea.

John Whidden, born in Massachusetts in 1832, expressed the feeling very well in his recollections of *Old Sailing Ship Days:*

Marblehead being a seaport town, my time, when not in school or employed around the house doing chores, was spent with my companions about the wharves, swim-

ming or climbing about the vessels at the docks, rowing around the harbor in the small boats, or dories, that we would borrow from the various captains or skippers of the fishing craft—mostly schooners from fifty to ninety tons burthen, engaged in the Grand Banks fisheries, of which at this time there was a fleet of nearly a hundred sail, all hailing from and owned in Marblehead.

What a treat for us boys when a square rigger—as we designated all barks, ships and brigs—came sailing into the harbor, perhaps from Cadiz, Spain, laden with salt for the fishing fleet to take to the Grand Banks of Newfoundland for their spring fares, and when she hauled into the wharf to discharge her cargo into the salt sheds how we youngsters swarmed on board exploring every nook and cranny of her, climbing over her rigging, daring each other to mount higher and higher until with a feeling of triumph I at last placed my cap on the main royal truck, the highest point, and looking down saw the admiring though envious gaze of my young companions!

Then, again, to sit around the fo'c'sle [forecastle of a ship] after the work for the day was over, to see the sailors at their meals, and hear them spin their yarns, was happiness indeed.

To go to sea, become a sailor, visit foreign lands, and in due time become the captain of a fine ship, this was the goal to be looked forward to, the great aim of our lives. It certainly was of mine, and I judge of all, or nearly all, of my playmates.

Charles Low, eight years older than Whidden, was born in Salem, Massachusetts, but brought up in Brooklyn, New York. He was the youngest son of one of the most successful merchant families in America. In his autobiography called *Some Recollections* Low begins, "I grew as other boys do, with the exception that I was, at a very early age, inclined to seek salt water. My mother told me that as soon as I could crawl I went for it, and I remember as far back as I remember anything that to be on and in the water was my supreme delight."

When he was twelve years old young Charles nearly ran away to sea. At this early age he felt

bound to go to sea, and I went to New York and got a berth on board of a brig bound to Savannah. Another boy went with me and meant to sail with me, but he backed out and so did I. I was very sorry, for I was passionately fond of the sea; and if I could only get something to float on I was happy. Even in winter I have been to Gowanus Bay and got on a cake of ice and paddled around.

Charles Low tried again, but one of his older brothers was too watchful: "Just before the steam tug cast off, I got into one of the [ship's] bread lockers in hopes they would not miss me, and thus I could get away to sea; but they were on the watch for me and my brother Josiah set the captain and mate after me who soon found me half suffocated, and sent me on board the tug."

His family did all they could to keep him from going to sea, but he scorned the wealth that he knew would be his if he cooperated with them.

My father took me as clerk in his store. He was a wholesale commission merchant in African and South Amer-

ican goods—gum copal, shellac, myrrh, aloes, peppers, and so forth. The store was in Fletcher Street. . . . Just opposite was a sailors' boarding-house; and I spent a good deal of my leisure time [there] . . .

I liked my work very much, but all the time I was planning to go to sea. . . . my father offered to take me into partnership when I was twenty . . . but I refused it. I could not give up the sea.

Charles Low and John Whidden were typical of thousands of youngsters living along the east coast in early nineteenth-century America; like many of them, they achieved their hearts' desire—command of their own ships. Unlike most, these two wrote excellent memoirs of their experiences.

Others kept diaries. Richard Henry Dana, Jr., born in Cambridge, Massachusetts, in 1815, kept a daily record of his two-year voyage in 1834–1835 around Cape Horn to what was then Mexican California. Five years later Dana's diary, with some editing and additional notes, was published under the title *Two Years Before the Mast*. It became one of the most famous books in America, the first time the point of view of the common sailor had ever been expressed.

Two Years Before the Mast was a veritable bible for young Charles Abbey, born in Brooklyn in 1841. Like Dana, Abbey kept an accurate record of his experiences and feelings as a sailor; that was in the 1850s, more than twenty years after Dana's voyage.

The accounts of these four young men give us a realistic picture of life at sea for a twenty-five-year span,

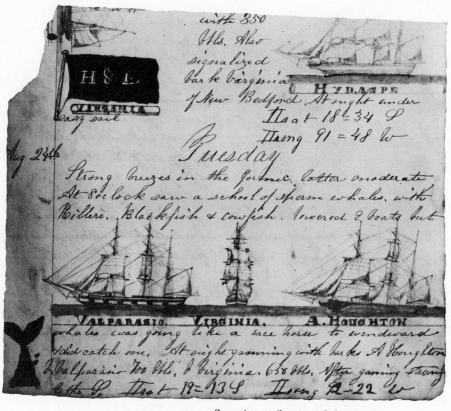

with 350
Bls. Also
signalized
bark Virginia
of New Bedford. At night under
easy sail

Aug 24th

Lat 18=34 S
Long 91=48 W

Tuesday

Strong breezes in the former. Latter moderate
At 8 o'clock saw a school of sperm whales, with
Killers. Blackfish & cowfish. Lowered 2 boats but
whales was going like a race horse to windward
I did catch one. At night gamming with barks A Houghton
2 Valparasio 700 Bls. & Virginia. 650 Bls. After gamming steering
to the S. Lat 19=43 S Long 92=22 W

Sometimes sailors recorded events by
drawing in their journals. Here, a "gam"—
a whaleship get-together at sea.

during which America rose to become the greatest maritime nation in the world. Many changes took place during the period. Ship design was vastly improved. Dana's little brig *Pilgrim*, barely over 180 tons, was slow compared to Abbey's *Surprise*, among the sleekest, fastest clippers ever built and over 1,500 tons. Laws were passed to protect seamen from mistreatment, largely through Dana's efforts. But the size and design of ships did not alter the sailor's life very much, nor were the laws very effective. Thus the experiences of all four were remarkably similar.

Abbey was quite as eager to get to sea as Low and Whidden, and like them advanced to become captain of his own ship. Dana went to sea for his health, and made only one voyage. He tells us nothing of his enthusiasm for going to sea, but he certainly indicates his eagerness to pass for an experienced sailor. And despite the difficult time he had, he developed a deep sentiment for both ships on which he sailed.

What was it about the sea that drew these four young men to it? The pay was very low, twelve dollars a month for an able seaman in Dana's day. In fact, for the first year they sailed as apprentice boys, and received no pay at all. The food was always monotonous, sometimes almost inedible. They endured terrible hardship, constant danger—death inches away awaiting the slip of a foot. They knew cruelty, sometimes suffering inhuman treatment at the hands of their officers.

In their recollections, neither Low nor Whidden gives more than a hint of ill treatment. But both Dana and Abbey have some bitter things to say on the subject.

Abbey, after vowing never to go to sea again, returned to make it his career. Why?

There were many reasons why young men went to sea, but most significant was the simple fact that the sea was their heritage. It had brought their forefathers to these shores in the first place. From the beginning, the early settlers had clung to the sea and its estuaries: without roads, water was the only practical means of transportation. Many an outlying family even went to church by "water horse," to use the term of an astonished English visitor to Salem in 1634 who described the water horse as "made of whole pine trees, being about two and a half feet over and twenty feet long. There be more canoes in this town than in the whole patant; every household having a water horse or two."

Two hundred years later roads were still poor, and scows with two- or three-man crews could haul cargoes that would require 40 wagons, 160 horses, and 80 teamsters to move overland. One little New England girl, Lucy Larcom, born in Beverly, Massachusetts, in 1824, wrote about her New England childhood:

An "arm of the sea" I was told that our river was, and it did seem to reach around the town and hold it in a liquid embrace. Twice a day the tide came in and filled its muddy bed with a sparkling flood. So it was a river only half the time, but at high tide it was a river indeed; all that a child could wish, with its boats and its sloops, and now and then that most available craft for a crew of children—a gundalow. We easily transformed the spelling into "gondola," and in fancy were afloat on Venetian waters, under some overhanging balcony, perhaps at the very Palace of the Doges—willingly blind to the reality of a mudscow leaning against some rickity wharf posts, covered with barnacles.

Beyond the river was the ocean, and Lucy had the same feeling for it as the boys. But Lucy was a girl. She watched her brothers go to sea; she could only daydream.

For some girls the dream became a reality. Susan Brock was born to it, a Nantucket captain's daughter who "doubled the Horn" (sailed around Cape Horn and back again) on her father's clipper *Midnight* when she was only six years old. "On one of the most memorable of these stormy days," she tells us,

Father came below and wrapping me warmly, took me in his arms and up on deck, and between driving snow squalls told me which way to look to see a point of land covered with snow and ice, saying, with much emphasis, "Now look hard and try to remember what you see, for there are not many little girls who ever see Cape Horn."

Others married the sea. After years of loneliness ashore, Eliza, wife of Captain Thomas Williams, chose life aboard with her husband on his whaling ship *Florida*.

September 7th, 1858. . . . Now I am in the place that is to be my home, possibly for 3 or 4 years; but I can not make it appear to me so yet it all seems so strange, so many Men and not one Woman beside myself; the little Cabin that is to be all my own is quite pretty; as well as I can wish, or expect on board of a Ship. I have a rose geranium to pet, that Mrs. Fish has been kind

enough to send me, and I see there is a kitten on board.
I think it will not all be as pleasant as it is today; the
motion of the Ship I shall be a long time getting used to.

But most girls along the coast were like Lucy Larcom;
they knew the sea only as a familiar neighbor with an
all-encompassing influence on the town.

The sea [said Lucy] was its nearest neighbor, and pene-
trated to every fireside, claiming close intimacy with
every home and heart. The farmers up and down the
shore were as much fishermen as farmers; they were as
familiar with the Grand Banks of Newfoundland as they
were with their own potato-fields. Every third man you
met in the street, you might safely hail as "Shipmate," or
"Skipper," or "Captain." My father's early seafaring experience gave him the latter title to the end of his life.

It was hard to keep the boys from going off to sea
before they were grown. No inland occupation attracted
them. "Land-lubber" was one of the most contemptuous
epithets heard from boyish lips. . . .

Men talked about a voyage to Calcutta, or Hong-Kong,
or "up the Straits"—meaning Gibraltar and the Mediterranean—as if it were not much more than going to the
next village. It seemed as if our nearest neighbors lived
over there across the water; we breathed the air of foreign
countries, curiously interblended with our own.

The women of well-to-do families had Canton crape
shawls and Smyrna silks and Turk satins, for Sabbath-day
wear, which somebody had brought home for them.
Mantel-pieces were adorned with nautilus and conch-
shells, and with branches and fans of coral; and children

had foreign curiosities and treasures of the sea for play-things. There was one imported shell that we did not value much, it was so abundant—the freckled univalve they called a "prop." Yet it had a mysterious interest for us little ones. We held it to our ears, and listened for the sound of the waves, which we were told that it still kept, and always would keep. I remember the time when I thought that the ocean was really imprisoned somewhere within that narrow aperture.

We were accustomed to seeing barrels full of cocoa-nuts rolled about; and there were jars of preserved tropical fruits, tamarinds, ginger-root, and other spicy appetizers, almost as common as barberries and cranberries, in the cupboards of most housekeepers.

We had foreign coins mixed in with our large copper cents—all kinds, from the Russian "kopeck" to the "half-penny token" of Great Britain. Those were the days when we had half cents in circulation to make change with. For part of our currency was the old-fashioned "nine-pence"—twelve and a half cents, and the "four pence ha'penny"—six cents and a quarter. There was a good deal of Old England about us still.

And we had also many living reminders of strange lands across the sea. Green parrots went scolding and laughing down the thimbleberry hedges that bordered the cornfields, as much at home out of doors as within. Java sparrows and canaries and other tropical song-birds poured their music out of sunny windows into the street, de-lighting the ears of passing school children long before the robins came. Now and then somebody's pet monkey would escape along the stone walls and shed-roofs, and try to hide from his boy-persecutors by dodging behind a chimney, or by slipping through an open scuttle, to the terror and delight of juveniles whose premises he invaded.

And there were wanderers from foreign countries domesticated in many families, whose swarthy complexions and un-Caucasian features became familiar in our streets —Mongolians, Africans, and waifs from the Pacific islands, who always were known to us by distinguished names— Hector and Scipio, and Julius Caesar and Christopher Columbus . . .

All along the Atlantic coast children lived and played within sight and sound and smell of the sea's commerce. Every little village had its wharves and shipyards, humming with activity.

Captain John Bradford, recollecting his boyhood days during the 1830s in the little coastal town of Duxbury, Massachusetts, recalled that even the schoolhouse he attended was "built on piles over marshy land where at every high tide the water flowed," and that:

From the little schoolhouse on Powder Point we young folks could hear the clatter and clangor of six shipyards all in full blast within less than a quarter of a mile. . . .

The nearest shipyard to the schoolhouse was the Drews', which was a double yard, where often two vessels were building at once. Many a wheelbarrow load of chips have I brought from that yard; many a time, at eleven o'clock in the forenoon and four in the afternoon, have I heard the call of "Grog O," whereupon all of the carpenters quit work and adjourned to the workhouse and "smiled";

many a time have I watched the launching of the vessels built there. . . . Of course school always adjourned for such an important event, which took place generally about 11 A.M. (high water, spring tides, full and change of the moon).

The most interesting part of the programme to us small boys was what we called "dashing the bottle." A man standing on the bowsprit holding by a short lanyard [rope] a bottle of wine or something of the sort, broke it over the bows just as the vessel took the water, at the same instant calling out: "Here's success to the good ship—'Oneco'!!"—for instance.

John Bradford's first job was working for Ezra Weston, who was known to his fellow townsmen as "King Caesar" because of the extent of his holdings.

His ships were then to be seen in all parts of the world. He not only built his own vessels, but he controlled nearly all the branches of business connected with ship-building and the ownership of vessels. He had his own ropewalk, sparyard, blacksmith shop and sail-loft; brought his timber and lumber from Haverhill and Bangor in his own schooners, or from Bridgewater and Middleboro with his own ox or horse teams, and his supplies from Boston in his own packets.

His salt came from Cadiz, St. Ubes, and Turk's Island in his own brigs. He sent his schooners to the Grand Banks for fish in the summer time, and "out South" in the winter for corn.

Like any boy of any era, John Bradford was not enthusiastic about his first job.

The period of schooling was brief in those days for the sons of hard working parents, and at a very early age I was released from the absorbing labor of fishing for minnows with a bent pin through the cracks of the schoolhouse floor, and set at the far more irksome task of "turning the wheel in the ropewalk."

A ropewalk was a long building in which rope was manufactured. A boy would turn the handle of a spinning wheel, or winch, while men backed down the walk feeding him hemp, which they were spinning into threads as they walked. By turning the winch, the boy "laid" the threads together into rope for running rigging, lines for hauling a ship's sails. Spinning the threads by hand, the men, about six at a time, each with a bunch of hemp tied to his waist, all moved with slow backward steps down the ropewalk. Bradford wrote:

It required a good deal of practice for a man to spin an even thread, with no weak spots or bunches in it. It was monotonous work, the spinning, and the boy turning the wheel that twisted the threads had a dull time of it; after the men had passed out of hearing he heard nothing but the rattle of his wheel for twenty minutes.

There is an old conundrum: "Why is a ship always called 'she'?" the correct answer to which is supposed to be: "Because it needs so much rigging." . . .

When one length had been spun the boy must take the separate threads off the wheel, splice two together, and hook them to a big post amidships of the walk, and then walk down the entire length (about three hundred yards), taking in a crotched stick the threads that had just been spun from the small hooks overhead where the spinners had put them, and laying them all together over into large hooks in the middle, just clear of a man's head.

Then the boy must carry a fresh supply of hemp to his wheel for the men to use for the next thread. From "sun to sun" this dull work went on, and that in the longest summer days meant from 4:30 A.M. to about 7:15 P.M., with half an hour allowed for breakfast and one hour for dinner.

No man, much less a boy, had strength enough to turn the spinning winch for laying in the heavy threads of the massive standing rigging, which supported a ship's masts. So a horse supplied the power.

When we were laying up [standing] rigging there was more excitement, and though the work was harder, I liked it better. Down in the cellar of the ropewalk I rode astride of "old Dick," who, harnessed to a long bar connected by a central upright "drum" with the heavy machinery above, walked round and round in a circle, thus supplying the needed power. A fine old horse, old Dick well deserved the substantial monument which still marks his grave in the sunny pasture near the scene of his labors, and bears this inscription:

"All are but parts of one stupendous Whole,
Whose body nature is, and God the soul."

Here lies buried honest Dick, who faithfully served three generations. This noble horse was born upon Powder Point, A.D. 1817. Here lived and here died 1846.

As Captain Bradford said, "The most natural step for a boy to take was from the ropewalk, or the wharf to the deck—or the masthead—of a vessel, and in this way I graduated into the more exciting and absorbing career at the early age of fifteen."

To comprehend the heights to which America had grown as a maritime nation, one need only multiply the activity in little Duxbury by that in hundreds of village seaports from Maine to Maryland and add to it the forests of masts clustered along the waterfronts of cities like Baltimore, Boston, and New York. Richard McKay in his *Maritime History of New York* points out that in that city during this period

ten thousand workmen were called to their labors every morning by the clang of the shipyard bells. William H. Webb and one or two other master builders employed each more than a thousand of the most intelligent and skillful mechanics whom the country had ever known, and the East River shipyards often had at the same time twenty or thirty great vessels on the stocks awaiting completion.

How, in the space of less than half a century, had America become such a maritime power?

From the very beginning the sea had been the economic lifeblood of New England. The Pilgrim fathers had never planned it that way. As chief stockholders in the Plymouth Company, they controlled all the land and had intended to pattern their life after the English estate system, with the poorer members of the company acting as tenant farmers and laborers.

Thus many of the settlers, who had sacrificed so much for freedom in this new land, found themselves not free but trapped. Working the thin New England soil as tenant farmers could be little better than serfdom. Hemmed in by the impenetrable forest, they could look only to the sea for a livelihood.

So they learned how to make dugout canoes, how to trap alewives—fish that swarmed by the millions up the streams to spawn in early summer—how to fish for cod and the dozens of other fish farther offshore. They began building their own boats, not only for fishing but for trade as well. The sea that had cut them off now set them free.

In addition, the very economy, or lack of it, forced the stockholders of the Plymouth Company to give up their dream of landed estates. As early as 1641 Governor Winthrop of Massachusetts wrote, "All foreign commodities grew scarce and our own of no price. Corn would buy nothing; a cow which cost last year £20 might now be bought for 4 or £5 . . . These straits set our people on work to provide fish, clapboards, plank, etc. . . . *and to look out to the West Indies for a trade.*"

The West Indian planters, with a slave economy devoted almost entirely to raising sugar cane, needed what New England had to offer: lumber, grain, and salt fish to feed their slaves. For a rebellious Yankee boy a West Indian voyage as a deck hand on a local sloop was wondrous escape from the repressions of Puritan society. No long dreary hours in church, no dull chores every day— work, yes, plenty of it, and danger and discomfort, but freedom of a sort he would never get at home.

Such voyages broadened the horizons of hundreds of Yankee boys—especially if the captain was enterprising and, instead of returning home with his cargo of sugar and molasses, crossed the Atlantic to trade his West Indian cargo at a good profit for English manufactured goods, then skipped back across the Atlantic for more profits from the sale of these sorely needed goods. Thus was laid the basis for the American merchant marine.

When the American Revolution came, many of these ships turned privateer, harrying British shipping. Then, at the end of the war, the sea captains and merchants who owned these vessels were faced with the task of rebuilding their world trade outside the protecting confines of the British Empire.

Bold captains, startlingly young and in ridiculously small vessels, sailed in search of new markets—around the Cape of Good Hope to the Orient. As early as 1783 Captain Hallet of Hingham, Massachusetts, set out for China in his little fifty-five-ton sloop *Harriet* with a load of ginseng, a medicinal root grown in the Hudson Valley and highly prized by the Chinese. He went no farther than the Cape of Good Hope, where some British East Indiamen, worried about possible Yankee competition in the China trade, bought the entire cargo for double its weight in tea.

A few months after the *Harriet* left Boston, the *Empress of China* sailed out of New York all the way to Macao on the Chinese coast, and returned with a profitable cargo of silks and teas. Then the *Hope* and the *Grand Turk*, both of Boston, sailed away to return with rich cargoes from Canton itself. By 1786 a Boston com-

During the Revolution the young American sailors had their counterparts in the British Royal Navy. Midshipman Augustus Brine, as painted by John Singleton Copley, enlisted at the age of twelve.

mercial house was established at Canton, the only city on the Chinese mainland in which the *fan kwai* ("foreign devil") was allowed to trade. It was the first challenge to British supremacy in the East.

But American merchants suffered one disadvantage: they lacked the proper goods to trade with. The Chinese had no use for lumber, salt fish, and grain, and young America was a poor nation, with no silver or gold to bargain with. Britain was wealthy: she had plenty of silver and her entire Eastern empire to draw on for goods that appealed to Chinese tastes. Americans had to pick up what they could where they could find it.

In 1787 a group of Boston merchants financed an around-the-world expedition to try to solve the problem. The eighty-three-foot ship *Columbia,* under Captain Kendrick, and the forty-five-foot sloop *Lady Washington,* under Captain Gray, sailed around Cape Horn and spent a year bargaining for sea-otter furs on Vancouver Island, off the western coast of Canada. Then Captain Gray took the *Columbia* on to Canton, successfully traded the otter skins for Chinese goods, and returned by way of the Cape of Good Hope. The problem of goods for the China trade was solved.

On her next voyage, in 1792, the *Columbia,* now under Captain Gray, made an even more important discovery, giving America claim to a huge new territory. Seventeen-year-old John Boit, one of the mates on the *Columbia,* told how they saw

an appearance of a spacious harbour abreast the Ship, haul'd our wind for it, observ'd two sand bars making off,

with a passage between them to a fine river. . . . We di-
rected our course up this noble River in search of a Vil-
lage. The beach was lin'd with Natives, who ran along
shore following the Ship. Soon after, above 20 Canoes
came off, and brought a good lot of Furs, and Salmon,
which last they sold two for a board Nail. The furs we
likewise bought cheap, for Copper and Cloth. . . . Capt.
Gray named this river Columbia's . . .

And it is the Columbia to this day. Thus the Yankee search for trade opened up Oregon and the entire Northwest for America's future.

As the Bostonians had taken over the American Northwest–China market, so Salem gained control of the East Indies trade—pepper, coffee, sugar, hemp, indigo. And like those on the Boston ships, the Salem crews were young. The ship *Benjamin* for instance, was commanded in 1792 by nineteen-year-old Nathaniel Silsbee, a poor boy who had risen to captain in five years. He went on to become president of the Massachusetts senate and a U.S. senator. His first mate was twenty, his clerk eighteen, and the oldest man on board was the second mate, age twenty-four.

But with the Napoleonic Wars between England and France in the 1790s, trouble began again. Both nations started to intercept American ships carrying supplies to the other. To protect her interests, young America expanded her navy.

True to the spirit of the new nation, the ships were fast and maneuverable, able to sail rings around the huge awkward warships of that time. American designer

Joshua Humphreys turned out such superb vessels as the *Constitution* and the *Constellation,* unconventional in appearance but very fast and destined to have an influence on later design.

In a tavern argument with some officers of an English frigate who were ridiculing the appearance of the *Constitution,* young Isaac Hull, her lieutenant in charge of seamanship, bet a cask of wine that his "fir built monster of a ship" could outsail theirs. They started at sunrise and by sundown the English frigate was "hull down," almost out of sight astern.

Then in 1807, to New England's horror, President Jefferson, in an attempt to keep out of a European war between France and Britain, placed an embargo that prohibited all trade with the embattled countries. New England went into a deep economic depression. For two years ships rotted at the wharves. Bitter Yankees sang,

> *Our ships all in motion once whitened the ocean,*
> *They sailed and returned with a cargo;*
> *Now doomed to decay, they have fallen a prey*
> *To Jefferson—worms—and embargo.*

The embargo was lifted in 1809, but when war was finally declared in 1812 England's blockade bottled up the ports again. The little American navy performed wonders against the huge British fleet, but could never hope to conquer it. It was the privateers who saved the country by harrying British shipping and capturing hundreds of enemy vessels.

Because of the remarkable performance of their men and ships during the war, Americans developed pride in

The America, *a fast privateer*
of the War of 1812.

their reputation as a maritime nation, and boys felt an ever deeper yearning for the sea. For mere boys had served in the crews of all the ships. David Farragut, who later became the great admiral, was appointed a midshipman at the age of nine. During the War of 1812 his ship *Essex* had seized so many enemy vessels in the South Pacific that there were hardly enough American officers to command them. Young Farragut was made prizemaster of one, the *Alexander Barclay*. In his diary he wrote, "When it was decided that I was to take the ship to Valparaiso, I felt no little pride at finding myself in command at twelve years of age."

With the new peace treaty most trade barriers were pushed aside. Shipping blossomed as never before, and yards sprang into existence up and down the Atlantic coast, turning out a steady stream of vessels. The stage was set; America was poised for her half century of supremacy at sea.

SEA LEGS

Backed by tradition and boundless enthusiasm, the boys set out to sea. But although tradition helped make sailors of them, it certainly did not turn them out full-blown. Their enthusiasm was considerably dampened by their first days' woeful experiences.

Richard Dana, proud in his new sailor outfit, was sure he looked like an experienced tar as he went aboard ship that momentous August day in 1834.

The fourteenth of August was the day fixed upon for the sailing of the brig "Pilgrim" on her voyage from Boston round Cape Horn to the western coast of North America. As she was to get under way early in the afternoon, I made my appearance on board at twelve o'clock in full sea-rig, with my chest, containing an outfit for a two or three years' voyage, which I had undertaken from a determination to cure, if possible, by an entire change of life, and by a long absence from books and study, a weakness of the eyes, which had obliged me to give up my pursuits, and which no medical aid seemed likely to cure.

The change from the tight dress coat, silk cap and kid

gloves of an undergraduate at Cambridge [Harvard], to the loose duck trousers, checked shirt and tarpaulin hat of a sailor, though somewhat of a transformation, was soon made, and I supposed that I should pass very well for a jack-tar. But it is impossible to deceive the practiced eye in these matters; and while I supposed myself to be looking as salt as Neptune himself, I was, no doubt, known for a landsman by everyone on board as soon as I hove in sight.

A sailor has a peculiar cut to his clothes, and a way of wearing them which a green hand can never get. The trousers, tight around the hips, and thence hanging long and loose round the feet, a superabundance of checked shirt, a low-crowned, well-varnished black hat, worn on the back of the head, with half a fathom of black ribbon hanging over the left eye, and a peculiar tie to the black silk neckerchief, with sundry other minutiae, are signs, the want of which betrayed the beginner, at once. Besides the points in my dress which were out of the way, doubtless my complexion and hands were quite enough to distinguish me from the regular salt, who, with a sunburnt cheek, wide step, and rolling gait, swings his bronzed and toughened hands athwartships, half opened, as though just ready to grasp a rope.

Brought up in the severe Puritan tradition, and a conscientious scholar, young Dana naturally took his new role as a sailor very seriously.

With all my imperfections on my head, I joined the crew, and we hauled out into the stream, and came to anchor for the night. The next day we were employed in preparations for sea, reeving studding-sail gear, crossing royal yards, putting on chafing gear, and taking on board our powder. On the following night, I stood my first watch. I remained awake nearly all the first part of the night from fear I might not hear when I was called; and when I went on deck, so great were my ideas of the importance of my trust, that I walked regularly fore and aft the whole length of the vessel, looking out over the bows and taffrail at each turn, and was not a little surprised at the coolness of the old salt whom I called to take my place, in stowing himself snugly away under the long-boat, for a nap. That was a sufficient lookout, he thought, for a fine night, at anchor in a safe harbor.

An offshore wind (west in Boston, Dana's home port) was ideal for starting a voyage. So he was in for a disappointment when, after "beating down the bay" against a southerly wind, the *Pilgrim* was forced to drop anchor for another day to await a favorable breeze. When the wind finally shifted, he saw action enough, to his utter confusion.

My watch [on deck] began at eleven o'clock at night, and I received orders to call the captain if the wind came out from the westward. About midnight the wind became fair, and, having called the captain, I was ordered to call all hands. How I accomplished this I do not know, but I am quite sure that I did not give the true hoarse boatswain call of "A-a-ll ha-a-a-nds! up anchor, a-ho-oy!" In a short time everyone was in motion, the sails loosed, the yards braced, and we began to heave up the anchor, which was our last hold upon Yankee land.

I could take but little part in these preparations. My little knowledge of a vessel was all at fault. Unintelligible orders were so rapidly given and so immediately executed; there was such a hurrying about, and such an intermingling of strange cries and strange actions, that I was completely bewildered. There is not so hopeless and pitiable an object in the world as a landsman beginning a sailor's life.

The following day young Dana stood at attention with his shipmates after the watches, or work shifts, had been chosen. He was listening to the *Pilgrim*'s Captain Thompson deliver his "short characteristic speech, walking the quarter-deck with a cigar in his mouth, and dropping the words out between the puffs":

"Now, my men, we have begun a long voyage. If we get along well together, we shall have a comfortable time; if we don't we shall have hell afloat. All you've got to do is to obey your orders and do your duty like men—then you'll fare well enough—if you don't, you'll fare hard enough—I can tell you. If we pull together, you'll find me a clever fellow; if we don't, you'll find me a bloody rascal. That's all I've got to say. Go below, the larboard watch!"

So began every voyage, the captain establishing in no uncertain terms his absolute authority as master of the ship, and with good reason: the lives of all aboard were dependent on his judgment. A good captain ran a "tight ship." Each man and boy knew his place, his responsibilities, and his relationship to everyone else on board. Each vessel was a little nation, self-sufficient when at sea, with a well-organized "government" functioning in behalf of the ship and her entire company.

Dana quickly learned that "the captain . . . is lord paramount. He stands no watch, comes and goes when he pleases, and is accountable to no one, and must be obeyed in everything, without a question, even from his chief officer." It was the first mate, Dana found, who actually ran the ship:

The captain tells him what he wishes to have done, and leaves to him the care of overseeing, of allotting the work, and also the responsibility of its being well done . . . He is also ex-officio, the wit of the crew; for the captain does not condescend to joke with the men, and the second mate no one cares for; so that when "the mate" thinks fit to entertain "the people" with a coarse joke or a little practical wit, everyone feels bound to laugh.

The second mate's job was, according to Dana, "a dog's berth . . . neither officer nor man . . . He is expected to maintain his dignity and to enforce obedience, and still is kept at a great distance from the mate . . . he eats and sleeps in the cabin but . . . at the second table, that is, makes a meal out of what the captain and chief mate leave."

As for the steward, the captain's servant, the crew did not consider him one of themselves, and so he was left to the captain's mercy. The cook fared better because he was the patron of the crew, and those in his favor could get their wet mittens and stockings dried, or light their pipes at the galley in the night watch. Finally there were the carpenter and sailmaker, who did not have to stand watch, but were busy all day and, unless all hands were called, could sleep in at night.

Just as Dana's first day had confused and bewildered him, so John Whidden's first watch brought such misery that he soon had second thoughts about the wisdom of going to sea. "The night was dark," he wrote,

the topmast stun'sail having been taken in, the yards were braced forward, while the wind began to freshen and the sea to rise. To'gallant sails were handed, and while the ship heeled over to the increasing wind, the salt spray began to fly across the fo'c'sle deck, drenching me, and as I had no oilskins on I was soon wet through. To add to all this, I began to have a squeamish feeling at my stomach, which rapidly increased until I lost all interest in any lookout, and stood clinging to the fo'c'sle capstan, looking aft, towards the cabin, cold, wet and miserable, feeling that, after all, I may have made a mistake in deciding to become a sailor. As I thought of our cozy parlor at home, with its glowing grate of anthracite, in front of which I had spent so many happy evenings reading my favorite books, or sailing imaginary voyages, and contrasted that picture with my present situation, I made up my mind that when the ship arrived at New York, if ever she did, like the prodigal son I would return home, if I had to walk.

Whidden had arrived a week early at Newburyport, Massachusetts, to ship aboard the *Ariel*, a 136-foot ship of 572 tons. His last Sunday at home in Marblehead had been spent all day in church—he does not say why. The next morning he and his uncle carried his sea chest down to the railroad station, and Whidden bought a ticket to Newburyport for six new half-dollars, which seemed a lot to him.

On arriving, he hired a conveyance and drove to the wharf with his chest. There was the *Ariel,* looking trim and spar. Indeed she might have, for this was not only Whidden's maiden voyage, but the *Ariel*'s as well. Built in Newburyport for the China trade, the ship was bound first for New York to take on a load of flour for Liverpool. From Liverpool, with a new cargo, she was to sail to China.

Since it was a week before sailing time, Whidden was employed at odd jobs around the nearly empty ship. Only the first and second officers and the carpenter were aboard—no cook either, and so he ate supper at Brown's Tavern near the wharf. But it was comfortable enough. He was all alone in the forecastle, but had brought a mattress, sheets, blanket, and comforter with him, and made up his bed "after the home pattern." The crew was expected from Boston at the end of the week.

They finally arrived. Whidden was just going off to Brown's Tavern for his supper. It was a wet December afternoon when

I heard a great commotion on the deck overhead. The companion doors were thrown open, and down rained chests, bags, and hammocks, wet and dirty, followed by the crew who had just arrived on the train from Boston.

There were about twenty men, of all nationalities, and as soon as they landed in the fo'c'sle they began pitching the bags and hammocks into the berths, all talking and

*Newburyport, just as John Whidden saw it
when he sailed out on his first voyage in 1846.*

swearing, for they were not in good humor, being about as wet as their luggage.

I had drawn up, and was standing on my little chest alongside my berth, when, without any ceremony or asking "by your leave," an old grizzled shellback tossed into my clean berth a wet, dirty bag and hammock.

Although I had stood, half in awe, watching the scene, not venturing a word, this act of old Tom's was too much, and laying my hand upon his arm I remonstrated: "Don't do that! You'll soil my sheets!"

Tom gave me a puzzled look for a moment, and exclaimed, "Who in thunder are you?"

I hastened to assure him that I was a sailor, one of the crew, and that was my berth, and my bed was made up. With a queer look he mounted my sea-chest and glanced into my berth. Never shall I forget his look of wonder, and the ineffable scorn conveyed in his tone as he turned around to his chum, and exclaimed with withering sarcasm, "Well I'm blessed, Joe" (only he didn't say "blessed"), "if the beggar ain't got sheets!"

I made no reply, but I felt that in his eyes, at least, I was no sailor, and when they had gone to supper, shortly after, off came the sheets and pillow cases, which were stored at the bottom of my chest, nevermore to do duty as bedding on that ship.

On April 13, 1856, twenty-two years after Dana's and ten years after Whidden's departure, Charles Abbey boarded the California clipper *Surprise*. Well named, the *Surprise* had been surprising and delighting her owners, A. A. Low & Bro. (the mercantile concern of Charles

1536239

*A full share in the life of the forecastle
made the boys feel like real sailors.*

Low's older brothers), for six years. At her launching in 1850 there had been gloomy waterfront predictions that she would capsize because she was to be launched fully rigged (most vessels were not rigged until they were in the water). But she had come down the ways in Samuel Hall's Boston shipyard, masts and yards gleaming, colors flying, church bells ringing, and her sleek lines (183 feet long, 39 feet wide, and 22 feet deep) bringing gasps of admiration from half of Boston assembled for the occasion. Built for the California gold-rush trade, on her maiden voyage the *Surprise* had set a new record for New York to San Francisco by making the 15,000-mile passage around Cape Horn in 96 days and 15 hours, cutting a day from the *Sea Witch's* previous record of 97 days. After a breakneck run of 46 days to load tea for Hong Kong, she had sped on to London to sell her cargo for a $50,000 *net* profit—net on her first voyage, meaning $50,000 clear for her owners, above and beyond all expenses including wages for officers and crew, and the building of the ship itself.

The *Surprise* would sail to Penang Island off the Malay Peninsula, on to Singapore, Hong Kong, and Canton. In Penang, Abbey would help oversee the loading of a cargo of rice and betel nuts, both highly prized on the China market, and watch several of his Chinese shipmates chew the pepper-plant nut until their teeth turned black.

But now such exotic scenes were only to be imagined. Writing in pencil on the lined pages of a commercial ledger, Charles Abbey logged his first few days of sea life:

April 13th Sunday This day I was too sick to notice anything in particular.

April 14 Monday Sea Sick still . . .

April 15 Tuesday Sea Sick still . . .

April 16 Wednesday Sea sick still . . .

April 17 Thursday Quite thick-headed yet . . .

April 18 Friday Sea sickness all gone, feel "tip top" all but a little homesick.

Poor Abbey! He had no sooner gained his sea legs than he was literally knocked back down again. The second mate in charge of Abbey's watch was a brutal "bucko mate," quick with his fists and feet in response to anything meeting his disapproval. Rough on all the men, the mate had singled Abbey out, probably because of his weakness from seasickness, striking him and throwing things at him. Finally, two days after feeling "tip top":

April 20 Sunday Tonight about 11 o'clock Mr. Dow the 2ᵈ mate set the watch at work getting the topmast studding sail boom aloft . . . one of the other boys (Wᵐ Scott by name) stood behind me & commenced to take it up. I had rather have gone aloft a great deal than stay on deck & was on the point of telling Scott to stop, when the 2ᵈ mate struck me with all his force in the back of the head & said, "G—d, d—m you will you let that boy take it aloft, will you, will you" at the same time knocking me down on the deck & springing upon me & striking me on the back & head with both hands & pounded me with his heel on the head all the time swearing fearfully. As soon as I could get up I started to go up aloft & he took out a belaying pin & would have struck me had he not found it to be iron instead of wood. I could not come out on the next watch [four hours later] my head was so sore. That he inwardly injured me I am confident for I find great difficulty in breathing. It was more than 12 times that he struck me.

As a result of this beating Abbey was sick on and off for another two weeks. On April 27 he vowed, "I have this day made up my mind that if I ever get to the good port of New York again & find my father alive I will go at anything he may set me to & persue it with as much dilligence as possible." Not until May 4, Sunday, could he accurately write, "Getting better at last, I think."

Hazing—that is, overworking or roughing up—a green hand was not uncommon; all the boys had their share of it, but none of them—Dana, Whidden, or Low—seemed to have suffered such bad luck as Abbey. On his return voyage aboard another ship, the *Charmer*, Abbey found himself under a sadistic captain among whose pleasures was urging his vicious dog to bite the boys. Of him Abbey wrote in his diary, " '*Captain Lucas*' is the most Noisy Dirty Bawdy Obscene wretch I ever came across. No one who has not sailed with him can imagine how far he carries it. He never opens his mouth but to yell as loud as possible & all his language is filthy."

Yet a few months after his return to New York, having "quit the sea forever," Abbey was aboard a California clipper, the *Henry Brigham*, under Captain Dow, whom he called "my very beau ideal of a Sea Captain." For the ship and her entire company Abbey had nothing but praise: "If ever a good ship with good officers & good food & good treatment sailed the ocean this is the one. I cant find cause for complaint at all. Every one is called by his right name & all are treated like men & gentlemen at that."

Harsh punishment in response to open rebellion was something sailors could accept, however grudgingly. But unjustified punishment, such as Dana witnessed aboard the *Pilgrim*, stirred deep resentment in crews. Dana tells of one occasion when Captain Thompson flogged a man for what he called impudence. A shipmate, John the Swede, had simply asked, "What are you going to flog that man for, sir?" and in a trice John found himself spread-eagled (lashed to the rigging), the captain standing red-faced with fury, rope in hand.

When he was made fast, he turned to the captain, who stood turning up his sleeves and getting ready for the blow, and asked him what he was to be flogged for. "Have I ever refused my duty, sir? Have you ever known me to hang back, or to be insolent, or not to know my work?"

"No," said the captain, "it is not that I flog you for; I flog you for your interference—for asking questions."

"Can't a man ask a question here without being flogged?"

"No," shouted the captain, "nobody shall open his mouth aboard this vessel, but myself"; and began laying the blows upon his back, swinging half round between each blow, to give it full effect. As he went on his passion

A sailor's life was always subject to the
whims and discipline of his officers.

increased and he danced about the deck calling out as he swung the rope—"If you want to know what I flog you for, I'll tell you. It's because I like to do it!—because I like to do it! It suits me! That's what I do it for."

The man writhed under the pain, until he could endure it no longer, when he called out, with an exclamation more common among foreigners than with us—"Oh, Jesus Christ, oh, Jesus Christ!"

"Don't call on Jesus Christ," shouted the captain; "He can't help you. Call on Captain T——. He's the man! He can help you! Jesus Christ can't help you now!"

But most of the boys' woeful experiences seemed in retrospect quite trivial, and sometimes funny. A typical bumbling mishap was John Whidden's first attempt to carry food to the crew in the forecastle. It was the custom for the boys to do such drudgery in the forecastle. They had to keep the bread barge filled by taking it aft to the steward when it was empty, and returning with it to the forecastle after meals. In short, a boy was subject to everyone's call.

The galley, located on deck amidships, was a considerable distance from the crew's quarters in the forecastle. Thus in stormy weather, carrying the coffeepot or the kid (a cradle-shaped wooden basin into which food was heaped) across the deck and down the companionway (the steep stairway to the forecastle) was a precarious operation indeed. It was on just such a stormy day, with his legs none too steady under him, that Whidden was making his way along the deck with the kid.

By making short tacks and holding on, with the help of one of the deck watch, I managed to get the pots of coffee and the "kid" (a small tub) of salt beef passed down safely, and was about to descend, when I was ordered to go and see if the cook had not got something besides "salt hoss" for breakfast.

Returning to the cook, he handed me out a long, broad, deep pan, filled to the brim with a compound called scouse, consisting of ship bread broken up and soaked until soft. This, with salt pork fat and molasses baked in the pan, was taken off the stove boiling and seething with hot grease.

Taking hold of each end, I essayed to reach the companionway, which I finally succeeded in doing, and bending over, and holding out the pan, I called out, "Here, somebody, take it, will you?"

Old Tom at that moment was directly underneath, bending over the "kid," engaged in cutting off, with a sheath-knife, a generous slice of beef. Without looking up, he growled, in answer to my call to take it, "Oh, don't be in a hurry, you cub, wait till somebody's ready to take it."

At this instant the ship gave a heavy lurch, my foot slipped, the hot mess ran over and burnt my hand, and I let go! The pan turned over, and with a crash landed on poor Tom's head, the scalding compound flying to every corner of the fo'c'sle. I was horrified. With a yell like a Comanche, old Tom leaped from under, but the mischief was done. From all parts of the fo'c'sle came a volley of oaths and imprecations that scared me. The urgent invitations to come down I respectfully but firmly declined, at least until they should become more calm, and started to argue it out from the companionway. In the meantime the deck watch, having been drawn together by the uproar below, were convulsed with laughter, evidently regarding it as a great joke.

When young Whidden finally dared venture down into the forecastle again, he "no sooner landed on the deck than I received a tap on the side of the head, which would have knocked me across the fo'c'sle, had I not been held up by a tap from old Tom on the other side." After such a scalding, old Tom might have given the boy still more punishment, had it not been time for their watch to go to work. Eight bells struck and the watch went up, grumbling at having lost their breakfast. Whidden was a discouraged boy.

Such were the trials of a greenhorn, but on the other hand, Whidden tells us, "Where a boy did his work willingly, without grumbling, the men were always ready to treat him well, teach him the mysteries of knotting and splicing, and everything pertaining to the work on shipboard, doing all in their power to instruct and make a sailor of him."

Charles Low, who on November 5, 1842, sailed out of New York City on the *Horatio*, had a much easier time adjusting to shipboard life than the other boys. In fact, he was the only one of the four who did not get seasick. Furthermore, as a child he had become friends with a first mate and spent all his time, when the mate was in port, aboard ship learning seamanship. So Low could fairly say, "I was a good sailor and knew just where to find a rope when I first went to sea." Nor was Charles Low quite so alone as the other boys on their first voyages: one of his older brothers and the brother's wife were passengers aboard the *Horatio*.

Still, like the others Low had to adjust to the sailor's rough life, close quarters, limited amusements, and, of course, the plainness and monotony of the food. "Mondays we had salt beef and bread for breakfast, dinner, and supper, with a mixture at breakfast called coffee, a quart to each one, boiled with molasses. It did very well to soak biscuit in, and after a while I could drink it and think it good."

On Tuesdays it was salt pork instead of beef for every meal, and every night there was tea, boiled like the coffee with molasses for sweetening. Like all sailors Low was fond of scouse (with which Whidden had scalded old Tom that stormy day), and once a week there was also boiled rice. Six large spoonfuls of molasses came with it; but, says Low, "The sailmaker used to . . . stint us boys if he could, so as to have more for himself." On the Sabbath, the food was the same as on weekdays, except that the flour pudding, or sailors' "duff," had a few raisins in it, "which made it plum pudding," according to Low.

Low wrote about his experiences many years after the voyage, but Charles Abbey was recording his day-by-day reactions, and he had no compliments for the food. " '*Starvation reigns supreme*' in reality here," he said. About the Sunday duff:

We have nothing to do of course but trim sail today & have "duff" for dinner. Oh with what significance does

that word "duff" ring on my ears. Ever after I shall re-
member it in connexion with the hardest spots in my life.
It is simply flour & water with dried apples mixed in &
the whole boiled down hard & heavy as lead in a canvas
bag. When first taken out of the bag it looks like a loaf
of white sugar as much as can be.

The daily staples on which sailors lived were sea bread
or biscuit, and salt beef or salt pork; the fact that the
men called their meat "salt horse" was an indication of its
quality. But they thrived on it. In fact, many a boy found
it the final cure for seasickness. As Dana said,

Here I cannot but remember the advice of the cook, a
simple-hearted African.
"Now," says he, "my lad, you are well cleaned out; you
haven't got a drop of your 'long-shore swash' aboard of
you. You must begin on a new tack—pitch all your sweet-
meats overboard, and turn to upon good hearty salt beef
and sea bread, and I'll promise you, you'll have your ribs
well sheathed, and be as hearty as any of 'em, afore you
are up to the Horn." . . .
I cannot describe the change which half a pound of
cold salt beef and a biscuit or two produced in me. I was
a new being.

Actually it was not so much the food itself that sailors
growled about. What they really resented was the special
privilege officers enjoyed in their mess. In comparison
with "fo'c'sle grub," cabin fare was sheer luxury: pancakes, fancy baked breads and cakes, fresh chicken, pork,
and beef. To add insult to injury, when the officers ran

out of fresh beef they took the best of the crew's salt beef. Dana pointed out indignantly, "Whenever a barrel is opened, before any of the beef is put into the harness cask, the steward comes up and picks it all over, and takes the best pieces (those that have any fat on them) for the cabin."

And whenever possible cabin meat was fresh, which, without refrigeration, meant carrying along a veritable livestock farm. Taken aboard for Dana's return trip from California were

four bullocks, a dozen sheep, a dozen or more pigs, and three or four dozen of poultry . . . all stowed away in their different quarters; the bullocks in the longboat, the sheep in a pen on the forehatch, and the pigs in a sty under the bows of the longboat, and the poultry in their proper coop, and the jolly-boat was full of hay for the sheep and bullocks . . .

We killed one of the bullocks every four days, so that they did not last us up to the line [equator]. We, or rather they, then began upon the sheep and the poultry, for these never came into Jack's mess. The pigs were for the latter part of the voyage, for they are sailors and can stand all weathers. . . .

We had an old sow on board, the mother of a numerous progeny, who had been twice round the Cape of Good Hope, and once round Cape Horn.

Seamen had reason to growl about the officers' food privileges, yet once they grew accustomed to their own salt beef they actually preferred it to the "long-shore *swash.*" When passengers aboard the *Horatio* were too seasick to eat, their fancy cabin food was sent forward to the men. Charles Low described his shipmates' reaction:

We had lots of cabin fare sent to the forecastle: turkeys, chickens, mutton, beef, pies and puddings, and the salt beef and pork was not dealt out. It was a feast to me, but two days were too much for the men, and they went aft in a body and told the Captain they did not ship to eat "cabin grub," and they would do no more work till they had their salt beef and pork again.

Any misadventure that the fine fare might suffer, however, was greeted with delight by the crew. When a heavy sea had battered the galley and swept their food into the scuppers, Dana wrote, "we took the loss of our beef very easily, consoling ourselves with the recollection that the cabin had more to lose than we; and chuckled not a little at seeing the remains of the chicken pie and pancakes floating in the scuppers."

John Whidden shared the same satisfaction with his shipmates aboard the *Ariel* when a couple of pet monkeys upset the officers' menu:

One day the steward had taken the dinner to the cabin table, leaving it to go to the galley. No one was below, and it being warm, the skylight over the table was off. Two of the larger monkeys were about the after rigging. They had apparently been watching the steward, and seeing the coast clear, descended, dropping down through the skylight, and seizing a pair of chickens, on which the captain and passengers were to dine, they sprang on deck, and in a twinkling were aloft, just as the steward returned from announcing dinner. On entering the cabin the chickens were missed, and looking up, the scamps were discovered in the mizzen top, chattering and grinning, while they looked down at their pursuers. Several men had jumped into the rigging to catch them, but their efforts were of no avail; the monkeys were too nimble, and finally running out on a yard arm, dropped the chickens, one going overboard and the other on deck in a condition hardly fit for the captain's table.

Of course the quality of the food varied—usually according to the owner's policy, or more particularly the captain's. A ship with a generous skipper "fed well," but she was a "hungry ship" if she had a pinchpenny in command. One old sea shanty (work song) warned, "She's a starvation packet, good God! Let her go!"

But occasionally seamen did get a taste of fresh meat. Every time a pig was slaughtered, it was the custom for the crew to get one meal from it, which they called a "whack of sea pie." And in good weather, seamen off watch could try their hand at fishing; the meal was brightened up considerably if a bonito, dolphin, or porpoise was hauled on board.

The crew's quarters were in the forecastle, forward near the bow of a ship. Not so the boys'. John Whidden, who started out living in the forecastle with his shipmates, was lucky. Usually the boys' ears were considered too tender for the rough sailor talk, so they were quartered in steerage, closer to the stern and the cabin, where the officers could keep an eye on them.

Steerage was the space between the upper and lower

decks where a ship's supplies were stored. Although it might be moderately comfortable on large vessels, on others, like Dana's little *Pilgrim*, steerage left something to be desired:

The steerage in which I lived was filled with coils of rigging, spare sails, old junk, and ship stores which had not been stowed away. Moreover, there had been no berths built for us to sleep in, and we were not allowed to drive nails to hang our clothes upon. The sea, too, had risen, the vessel was rolling heavily, and everything was pitched about in grand confusion. There was a complete "hurrah's nest," as the sailors say, "everything on top and nothing at hand." A large hawser had been coiled away upon my chest; my hats, boots, mattress and blankets had all fetched away and gone over leeward, and were jammed and broken under the boxes and coils of rigging. To crown all, we were allowed no light to find anything with . . .

Two months later, as the *Pilgrim* rounded Cape Horn, Richard Dana and one of his steerage mates finally graduated to the forecastle. Dana was delighted.

We now began to feel like sailors, which we never fully did when we were in steerage. While there, however useful and active you may be, you are but a mongrel—and sort of afterguard and "ship's cousin." You are immediately under the eye of the officers, cannot dance, sing, play, smoke, make a noise, or growl [complain]. . . .
No man can be a sailor, or know what sailors are, unless he has lived in the forecastle with them—turned in

and out with them, eaten of their dish and drunk of their cup.

Dana adds that "another thing which you learn better in the forecastle than anywhere else is to make and mend clothes, and this is indispensable to sailors." With voyages lasting two or three years, clothes not only needed mending but replacing as well. This was done by taking old clothes apart at the seams and laying them out on light canvas provided by the sailmaker. After sketching out the shapes with charcoal, the sailors would cut the canvas, sew it together, and lo! new tarpaulin clothes. As Dana and his shipmates prepared for the long voyage home from the California coast, they were very busy indeed.

Our forecastle looked like the workshop of what a sailor is—a Jack-of-all-trades. Thick stockings and drawers were darned and patched; mittens dragged from the bottom of the chest and mended; comforters made for the neck and ears; old flannel shirts cut up to line monkey jackets; southwesters lined with flannel, and a pot of paint smuggled forward to give them a coat on the outside; and everything turned to hand; so that, although two years had left us but a scanty wardrobe, yet the economy and invention which necessity teaches a sailor, soon put each of us in pretty good trim for bad weather . . .

All such activity took place on a sailor's own time, during his "watch below," when he was off duty. On duty, the watch watched over the ship—to keep her on course, handle sail, perform necessary maintenance, and keep a weather eye out for danger.

The crew was divided into two watches, each one alternating four hours on and four hours off. Eight bells were struck at 4 o'clock, 8 o'clock, and 12 o'clock, day and night, to signal the change of the watch. Bells were also struck every half hour—one bell for 12:30, two bells for 1 o'clock, three bells for 1:30, and so on until eight bells called out the new watch at 4 o'clock. Then the process began all over again: one bell for 4:30, two bells for 5 o'clock, around the clock with eight bells struck every four hours. Thus at any hour of the day or night a sailor could tell by the number of bells how much longer he had to rest if he were in the watch below, or to work if he were on watch on deck.

With every twenty-four hours divided like this into six watches, a seaman would have been on duty during the same hours, day and night, through an entire voyage—how unfair to those on midnight watch! Thus the "dog-watch," which Dana describes so beautifully:

So that the same watch need not be on deck at the same hours . . . the watch from four to eight P.M. is divided into two half, or dogwatches, one from four to six; and the other from six to eight. By this means they divide the twenty-four hours into seven watches instead of six, and thus shift the hours every night. As the dog-watches come during twilight, after the day's work is done, and before the night watch is set, they are the watches in which everybody is on deck. The captain is up, walking on the weather side of the quarter-deck, the chief mate on the lee side, and the second mate about the weather gangway. The steward has finished his work in the cabin, and has come up to smoke his pipe with the cook in the galley. The crew are sitting on the windlass or lying on the forecastle, smoking, singing, or telling long yarns. At eight o'clock, eight bells are struck, the log is hove, the watch set, the wheel relieved, the galley shut up, and the other watch goes below.

LEARNING THE ROPES

A boy's confusion in adjusting to life aboard paled before his utter bewilderment in the face of maneuvering the ship itself. Here is how Richard Dana describes his first attempt to reef, or shorten, sail:

When I got up on deck a new scene and a new experience was before me. The little brig [Pilgrim] was close hauled upon the wind and lying over as it seemed to me nearly on her beam ends. The heavy head sea was beating against her bows with the noise and force almost of a sledge hammer and flying over the deck, drenching us completely through. The topsail halyards had been let go, and the great sails were filling out and backing against the masts with a noise like thunder. The wind was whistling through the rigging, loose ropes flying about; loud and, to me, unintelligible orders constantly given and rapidly executed, and the sailors "singing out" at the ropes in their hoarse and peculiar strains. In addition to all this I had not got my "sea legs on," was dreadfully sick, with hardly strength enough to hold on to anything, and it was "pitch dark." This was my state when I was ordered aloft, for the first time, to reef topsails.

*How I got along I cannot now remember. I "laid out"
on the yards and held on with all my strength. I could
not have been of much service . . . having been sick
several times before I left the topsail yard. Soon all was
snug aloft, and we were again allowed to go below.*

Little wonder Dana was confused. Of course he knew
the basics—they all did. A full-rigged ship, whether she
was a clipper, a packet, or a whaler, was a three-masted
vessel with square sails on all three masts. (Dana's vessel
was a brig, exactly like a ship, but with only two masts.)
Just as today, the hull was the body of the ship, the bow
its forward end, the stern its after end, the waist its middle section. Starboard was the right side of the vessel;
larboard—which is called port today—was the left.

The three masts were called foremost (forward),
mainmast (middle), and mizzenmast (aft). Actually,
each of these was made up of a series of shorter masts,
the top of each mast clamped to the bottom of the one
above. At deck level was the lower mast, to which was
fastened the topmast, which in turn supported the top-
gallant-mast. Next came the royal mast and finally the
little skysail mast. On Charles Abbey's *Surprise* the skysail mast rose 180-odd feet above the deck. The masts
were supported by standing rigging, or stays, heavy lines
running from a ship's sides to the tops of the masts.

All the square sails, except the three lowest, took their
names from the section of the mast on which they were
carried. So the sail on the fore-topmast was the fore-
topsail, the main-topsail was on the main-topmast, and
the mizzen-topsail was on the mizzen-topmast. The low-

The clipper Great Republic. *Note how the masts are joined one above the other. On this late clipper, however, the topsails and topgallant sails were "split" for easier handling. Reading from bottom to top: mainsail, lower topsail, upper topsail, lower topgallant sail, upper topgallant sail, royal.*
Compare with the America, page 24.

est sails were named foresail, mainsail, and cross jack—collectively called the courses.

The top edge of each square sail was laced with ropes onto a wooden pole called a yard, the center of which was fastened at right angles to the mast. The sail's lower corners, or clews, were hauled to the ends of the yard below by "sheets," rope lines that ran through pulleys (called end blocks) on the yard below, then to another block on the mast, thence to the deck. There the crew made the lines fast by tying them to belaying pins in the fife rail around the foot of the mast. Add to all this the spanker (a sail that stuck out alone on the stern and spanked the ship along), the staysails and jibs (triangular sails whose leading edges were fastened to the forward stays), and it is easy to see why Richard Dana or any young sailor might be confused on his first day at sea.

One of a sailor's main jobs was to set the sails—position and spread them to catch the wind. Dana's *Pilgrim*, though only a small brig, still had eighteen sails to be set. By the time the *Pilgrim*'s anchor was weighed and the ship under way, more than a hundred lines of running rigging had to be hauled, belayed (tied), and neatly coiled down. The big clipper *Surprise*, on which fourteen-year-old Abbey sailed, would have twenty-five to thirty-five sails aloft in a fair wind, with over 150 lines to handle—any one of which young Abbey had to be able to find on an instant's notice on the darkest night. An experienced sailor could count his way down the pin rail of any ship with his eyes closed, because on ships of all nations lines were belayed to belaying pins in exactly the same order.

Weighing anchor itself was a tremendous job: winding in half a mile of chain to pull a thousand ton ship to the point directly over the anchor (sailors call this hove short), then breaking the four-ton anchor out of the mud and hauling it up to the hawsepipe—all by hand! Not a direct pull, of course. With a few turns of the chain around the drum of a windlass, several men could work the anchor in. Or, on some ships, the chain was wound around a capstan, its removable capstan bars extending from it like spokes from the hub of a horizontal wheel. The crew would heave their chests against the bars, marching around the capstan to the rhythm of a capstan shanty:

So heave up the anchor, let's get it aweigh,
It's got a good grip, so heave, bullies, 'way—ay!

Once the anchor was hove short, the sails were unfurled; as soon as the anchor was broken out of the bottom, the headsails (forward sails) were "backed" against the wind. This pushed the bow of the ship down to the point where the wind was perpendicular to the vessel's course—called abeam. Then the foreyards were swung around to their regular sailing position, all sails were trimmed in, and the ship was under way.

After all sails were set, the crew could handle them with lines from the deck. But with heavy winds, all hands must scamper aloft to reef (shorten) and furl (roll up) some of the canvas—a routine matter once a sailor had learned his trade, but under extreme conditions it could be a very risky business even for an experienced hand. He who goes up must come down, preferably under his

Overhauling a line aloft on the Daisy,
*a later brig probably about the size
of Dana's* Pilgrim.

own power down the ratlines (rope ladders in the standing rigging), or sliding down a backstay.

On one occasion John Whidden took an unexpected shortcut that almost finished his career. On board the bark *Antelope*, bound for New York around Cape Horn, he was ordered aloft to furl an ice-encrusted sail during one of the winter storms that are so prevalent off that desolate cape.

Standing near the main rigging, I procured a gasket [a rope to tie up a furled sail] and started aloft. I was very heavily dressed, in thick clothing and monkey jacket with oil skins all over, thick seaboots and mittens. Opposite the spencer gaff, just under the maintop, I was obliged to swing out from the rigging, grasp the running gear, and with legs wound about the sail to smother it. I worked with both hands at getting the gasket passed. As I could do nothing with mittens on, I dropped them, and during the sharp heavy rolls, I would cling on with my fingers like fish hooks. Just as the last turns were passed and the sails secured, the barque gave an unusually heavy roll. My benumbed fingers, stiff with the cold, refused to hold on, and down I went by the run, and now my thick clothing and heavy sea-boots saved me. Striking the edge of the pinrail around the mainmast with my heels, and breaking a piece out, I shot into the scupper, striking my shoulder, but not my head.

Although not seriously injured, I lay there, stunned, the breath being knocked out of my body, and picking me up the watch carried me into the cabin, where I soon recovered my wind. Captain Crosby, after an examination, finding no bones broken, and nothing worse than a severe shaking up, administered to me a stiff glass of brandy, and I resumed my watch on deck, though feeling the effects in a general soreness for days after.

Once she was under way, sailing a ship on a straight course with a fair wind was a relatively simple matter. But against headwinds, a sailor's work was cut out for him. No sailing vessel can ever go directly into the eye of the wind: her sails will be blown aback, and she will be pushed backward. But she can sail to within a little less than forty-five degrees of the wind, and "tack" a zigzag course across the sea. Thus a vessel may sail on a starboard tack (wind coming from the starboard, or right side) for several hours or days; then she will come about, swing her yards around, and sail on a larboard tack (wind coming from the larboard, or left side).

Aboard a square-rigger, coming about and changing tacks was an intricate operation requiring great skill. Even the redoubtable Charles Abbey gave up any attempt to describe tacking, but referred to Richard Dana's account written twenty-one years earlier.

May 25 Sunday [1856] This is the 3^d uncomfortable Sunday we have had in succession. We tacked ship 3 times today & of course had to "roust out" all hands to perform the operation. For a description of all the orders you must look at "Two years before the mast" where the operation is all very minutely described. My station is at the Lee cross jack braces which it is my duty to haul round assisted by the other boys.

Tacking required the entire crew, so, as Abbey says, they had to roust out all hands, often in the middle of a sound sleep. But usually the four hours of the watch below were undisturbed unless a critical situation arose or a sudden worsening of the weather required all hands to shorten sail.

Abbey gives a graphic account of just such a situation en route to China.

It was one evening in the month of June 1856, that the good ship Surprise was off the Cape of Good Hope. I was standing by the mizzen royal halyards & the mate was pacing the poop in expectation of a change in the wind very soon, as the sky was dark & lowering & banks of mist kept rising incessantly. Just as 1 bell struck he stopped & looked steadily to windward. At this junction the captain came on deck & cast a hurried glance around till his eye rested in the same spot as the mates. He looked no longer but sang out at the top of his lungs, "Clew up the royals." In one instant I had let go the mizzen which I had all ready & ran up to the topgallant mast head & furled it. Before I was done I heard the topgallant yards rattle down, & I lent a hand to furl one. Then I went down on deck & laid up the ropes. By this time it was blowing & raining quite hard. All hands then stood by for a call. At 4 bells the mate sang out, "Call the Watch" & soon they came tumbling up from below to lend us a hand in reefing down, which operation was performed in about 50 minutes. Then being under snug sail the watch went below. Shortly after it struck 8 bells & I went

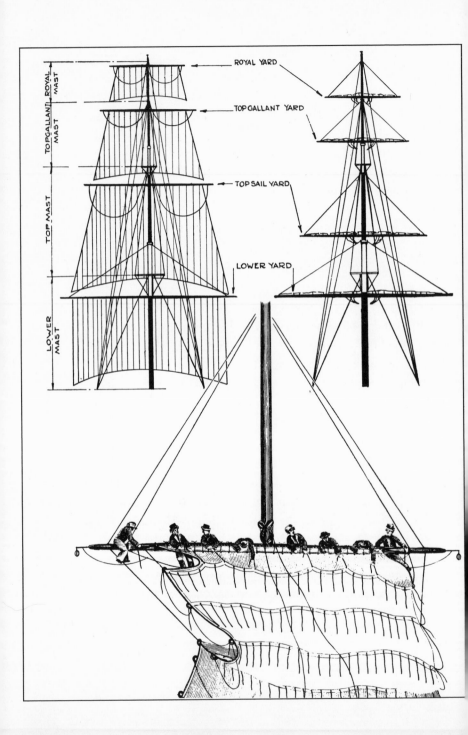

ROYAL YARD

TOPGALLANT YARD

TOP SAIL YARD

LOWER YARD

ROYAL MAST

TOPGALLANT MAST

TOP MAST

LOWER MAST

below. When I came on deck again the sky was clear, the stars were shining & we were under skysails once more.

Let's glance at what Abbey described. To the left is a sketch of the mizzenmast with all sails set except the skysail, and of the same mast with all sails furled.

To the order "Clew up the royals," Abbey had "let go the mizzen which I had all ready & ran up to the topgallant mast head & furled it." The *mizzen royal yard,* to which the royal sail was laced, was hauled aloft by a line called the *mizzen royal halyard* and then belayed to a pin in the *fife rail* at the foot of the mizzenmast. Abbey had untied this line from the pin and let the yard drop to the *topgallant-masthead.* Then he scrambled aloft to *furl* the royal, hauling the *clews* in to the center, rolling the sail up into a *bunt,* and making it fast with several turns of a *gasket* (rope). When he "heard the topgallant yards rattle down," it was the *topgallant sails* with their supporting yards dropping down to the *topmasthead* for furling.

Richard Dana, aboard the *Pilgrim* rounding South America for California, gives an even more dramatic account of reefing during one the dreaded storms known as pamperos, off the east coast of Argentina.

We met with nothing remarkable until we were in the latitude of the river La Plata. Here there are found violent gales from the southwest called Pamperos, which are very destructive to the shipping in the river, and are felt for many leagues at sea. They are usually preceded by lightning. The captain told the mates to keep a bright

---

Above, sails as they would look before and after furling.
Below, sailors are shown reefing.

lookout, and if they saw lightning at the southwest, to take in sail at once. We got the first touch of one during my watch on deck. I was walking in the lee gangway, and thought that I saw lightning on the bow. I told the second mate, who came over and looked out for some time. It was very black in the southwest, and in about ten minutes we saw a distinct flash. The wind, which had been southeast, had now left us, and it was dead calm. We sprung aloft immediately and furled the royal and topgallant sails, and took in the flying jib, hauled up the mainsail and trysail, squared the after yards, and awaited the attack. A huge mist capped with black cloud came driving toward us, extending over that quarter of the horizon, and covering the stars, which shone brightly in the other part of the heavens. It came upon us at once with a blast, and a shower of hail and rain, which almost took our breath from us. The hardiest was obliged to turn his back. We let the halyards run, and fortunately were not taken aback. The little vessel "paid off" from the wind, and ran on for some time directly before it, tearing through the water with everything flying. Having called all hands, we close-reefed the topsails and trysail, furled the courses and jib, set the fore-topmast staysail, and brought her up nearly to her course, with the weather braces hauled in a little, to ease her.

This was the first blow, that I have seen, which could really be called a gale. We had reefed our topsails in the Gulf Stream, and I thought it something serious, but an older sailor would have thought nothing of it. As I had now become used to the vessel and to my duty, I was of some service on a yard, and could knot my reef point as well as anybody. *I obeyed the order to lay aloft with the rest, and found the reefing a very exciting scene . . .*

Working ship could be quite as exhausting in calm weather too, especially on a clipper when speed to market might enhance not only the value of a cargo, but also the pride and reputation of her Yankee skipper bent on setting a record. Abbey's *Surprise* was very fast, and as noted, on her first voyage had set a record for the New York to San Francisco passage. Like all clipper-ship masters, Captain Ranlett was eager for a new record. So in good weather every scrap of sail on the *Surprise* was pressed on. Then, if the weather blew up, down it had to come again—especially such light sails as the studding-sails, very billowy ones set on long booms extending from the ends of the yards. It was no simple task; as Abbey described it, he crept "out on the yard (a ticklish place) & laid flat hold on with my feet . . ." No less precarious was his job of tending the highest sail on the ship, the skysail.

June 22 Sunday A beautiful day & 1st one for a Sunday we have had in a good while. Employed my time in reading & putting on a button here and there. I have been appointed Mizzen Skysail boy & have to loose, furl, & bend the sail, send the yard up or down as the case may be & in fact have the entire charge of the yard during my watch on deck. One of the boys in the other watch tends to it the rest of the time. It is an awful job when the ship is pitching to go up & loose or furl it for being so high up & the foot ropes too short the halyards loose on deck & the mast in the same state as the British left the old flag staff on the battery N.Y. upon evacuating it,* you can get nothing but your finger nails & eyelids to hold on'to. Many a time I have been "almost" gone when another lurch would bring me back only to have the operation repeated. "When one gets up there he is well tired with the exertion of climbing so high & then to have to balance himself upon his stomach on the yard & "pick up" 44 yards of canvass stow it & pass his gaskets make them fast & get down on deck in about 5 minutes & then perhaps be told he must do it quicker, it is hard. But all this is comprised in "Going to Sea" & any one who is fool enough to go must take his share of it.

Tending studdingsails and skysails might be exhausting and dangerous work for the boys, but it was never dull. What they really hated were such messy, tedious jobs as holystoning the decks with sandstone to make them white, tarring the rigging, or tending the pigs. Charles Low escaped this last because of his ability to perform more skilled tasks—thanks to his sailor friend who had taught him so much before he went to sea—but he couldn't escape the worst of them:

I found my knowledge helped me very much for the other boys had to feed the pigs and fowls and do the dirty work, though to be sure I had to do the slushing the masts with them, which is the worst and dirtiest of all the duties a boy is called upon to do. The topsail, topgallant, and royal yards hoist up and down, a peril, or band, keeping

---

* During the revolutionary war, the British had left it greased to make it difficult for the Americans to raise their flag.

them to the masts; and the masts must be well slushed or greased to have them move easily, and they must be slushed at least once a week. It is generally a Saturday's job. The boy, one for each mast, has an oyster tin or some other tin holding a quart or more of slush which he has to get from the cook. Now this is his first trouble, for the slush is the cook's perquisite, because it is the grease which comes from boiling the men's beef and pork. Some cooks will make ten or twelve barrels during a year's voyage, and they do not like the boys to touch it, and they swear at them if they drop or waste it. After getting the slush the boy has to provide a piece of flannel to rub it on the mast with. Now for a greenhorn or a boy to take this can of slush to the masthead without spilling some on his shirt bosom or on his pants, or getting it on his hands, is a very difficult job. Going up the rigging that has ratlines to step on, such as the lower and topmast rigging, is very well; but when you get to the topgallant rigging, where there are only two shrouds to climb up, and then to the royal and skysail masts, with only one rope to climb, then comes the trouble. If you can get safely to the skysail masthead without grease on your hands you are fortunate.

This was only one of endless tasks that filled the sailor's day. The officers saw to it that there was very little rest for Jack.

When I first left port [Dana tells us], and found that we were kept regularly employed for a week or two, I supposed that we were getting the vessel into sea trim and that it would soon be over, and we should have nothing to do but to sail the ship; but I found that it continued so for two years, and at the end of the two years there was as much to be done as ever. As has often been said, a ship is like a lady's watch, always out of repair.

All the gear and running and standing rigging had to be replaced, overhauled, and repaired in a thousand different ways.

There is also such a connection between different parts of a vessel, that one rope can seldom be touched without altering another. You cannot stay a mast aft by the backstays without slacking up the head stays, etc., etc. If we add to this all the tarring, greasing, oiling, varnishing, painting, scraping, scrubbing which is required in the course of a long voyage, and also remember this is all to be done in addition to watching at night, steering, reefing, furling, bracing, making and setting sail, and pulling, hauling and climbing in every direction, one will hardly ask, "What can a sailor find to do at sea?"

If, after all this labor—after exposing their lives and limbs in storms, wet and cold, the merchants and captains think that they have not earned their twelve dollars a month (out of which they clothe themselves), and their salt beef and hard bread, then they keep them picking oakum—ad infinitum.

However he might curse the danger and exhausting work aloft, or the unending repair, the sailor had a real appreciation of the beauty of his ship—although, as Dana points out, he rarely had the opportunity to see her under full sail:

A ship never has all her sail upon her, except when she has a light, steady breeze, very nearly, but not quite, dead aft, and so regular that it can be trusted, and is likely to last for some time. Then, with all her sails, light and heavy, and studding sails, on each side alow and aloft, she is the most glorious moving object in the world. Such a sight, very few, even some who have been at sea a good deal have ever beheld; for from the deck of your own vessel you cannot see her, as you would a separate object.

But one night Richard Dana did see it. The *Alert* (the brig on which he made his return voyage), homeward bound in the South Atlantic, had all sails set to capture every breath of the gentle southerly breeze.

One night, while we were in these tropics, I went out to the end of the flying jib boom, upon some duty, and, having finished it, turned round, and lay over the boom for a long time, admiring the beauty of the sight before me. Being so far out from the deck, I could look at the ship, as at a separate vessel—and there rose up from the water, supported only by the small black hull a pyramid of canvas, spreading out far beyond the hull, and towering up almost, as it seemed in the indistinct night air, to the clouds.

The sea was as still as an inland lake; the light trade wind was gently and steadily breathing from astern; the dark blue sky was studded with the tropical stars; there was no sound but the rippling of the water under the stem; and the sails were spread out, wide and high; the two lower studding sails stretching, on each side, far beyond the deck; the topmast studding sails, like wings to the topsails; the topgallant studding sails spreading fearlessly out above them; still higher, the two royal studding sails, looking like two kites flying from the same string; and highest of all, the little skysail, the apex of the pyramid, seeming actually to touch the stars, and to be out of reach of human hands. So quiet, too, was the sea, and so steady the breeze, that if these sails had been sculptured marble, they could not have been more motionless. Not a ripple upon the surface of the canvas; not even a quivering of the extreme edges of the sail—so perfectly were they distended by the breeze.

I was so lost in the sight, that I forgot the presence of the man who came out with me, until he said (for he too, rough old man-of-war's man as he was, had been gazing at the show), half to himself, still looking at the marble sails—"How quietly they do their work!"

HOME ON THE ROLLING DEEP

Whatever your feelings may be, you must make a joke of everything at sea; and if you were to fall from aloft and be caught in the belly of a sail, and thus saved from instant death, it would not do to look at all disturbed, or to make a serious matter of it.

So writes Dana, and the other boys—Whidden, Abbey, and Low—tell similar anecdotes. The foremast hands could enjoy a laugh on themselves or on a shipmate— whether he was swept into the scuppers by a heavy sea, or lost his food from a sudden lurch, or even found himself "hanging on by his eyelids" aloft with death staring up at him 160 feet below. Laughter, not sympathy, was the order of the day; life at sea was a continual hazard. It would never do to dwell on it too seriously, for what happened to the next man might someday happen to you —if it hadn't already.

But it wasn't all work. Without recreation, without a good story, a good song, a bit of whittling, or even a good book for those who could read, the men would have dropped from the yards in exhaustion. During the dog-watch and the watch below a song was always popular;

Occasionally there was time for such artistic pursuits as "scrimshaw"—the carving and etching of whalebone or whale's teeth.

below deck many a favorite was accompanied by a harmonica, a fiddle, a concertina, a pipe, or a penny whistle. On deck, as the sailors heaved on the capstan or at the lines, songs were almost indispensable. These work songs were called shanties. There was no inspiration to be had in a simple one-two-three-heave, but a song with just the right words to fit the mood of the moment would so strike the fancy of the crew that they would heave with a will.

Usually vessels had at least one shantyman, a sort of unofficial song leader. He could be the most valuable man on a ship. Along with a strong back, a throat of brass, and a blacksmith's bellows for lungs, he needed a remarkable sense of timing and an intuitive feeling for the mood of his men (to be sure to choose the right song for each situation), to say nothing of judging the temper of the officer on watch.

The shantyman might sing:

and the crew would roar in chorus:

At the word "cook"—who may have just served them a dreadful meal—every man would throw his weight into the job, usually hurling the bunt of a sail on top of a yard for this particular shanty.

Or, on a ship with a notoriously rough captain:

SHANTYMAN: It's quickly lay aloft to the break of the poop!
CHORUS: To me way! hay! BLOW the man down!
SHANTYMAN: Or I'll help you along with the toe of me boot!
CHORUS: Give me some time to BLOW the man down!

At the word "blow," which meant knock a man down, all hands would throw their weight on the halyard as they gradually hauled a yard to the masthead for setting another sail.

Or, for a light halyard pull, such as hoisting a jib, they might poke fun at the bo'sun:

Cheer'ly Man!

Oh, Nan-cy Daw-son, hi-oh! __ CHEER'-ly, man!
She's got a no-tion, hi-oh! __ CHEER'-ly, man!
For our old bo'-sun, hi-oh! CHEER'-ly, man!
Oh! Haul-ee hi-oh, __ CHEER'-ly, man!

Or jestingly complain of a misadventure ashore:

> Oh, Sally Rackett, hi-oh!
> CHEER'ly man!
> Pawned my pea jacket, hi-oh!
> CHEER'ly man!
> And sold the ticket, hi-oh!
> CHEER'ly man!

If the ship was leaking badly, they would sing a sarcastic comment on the vessel's sodden condition while they heaved away at the pumps:

Fire Down Below

FIRE! Fire! FIRE down be-low! It's FETCH a buck-et of wa - ter, girls, There's FIRE down be - low.

There is FIRE in the bilge, There's FIRE un-der the bow, There's NO FIRE in the fo' - c'sle, It's COLD down there you know.

When a spree ashore left some of the crew in no fit condition for work, their shipmates, forced to do double duty, would sing out sweet revenge as they ran the full length of the deck, rope in hand, bellowing out their favorite stamp-and-go shanty to the rhythm of their pounding feet:

The Drunken Sailor

Toss him by the leg with a running bowline,
Toss him by the leg with a running bowline,
Toss him by the leg with a running bowline,
Early in the morning.

CHORUS

Shave his belly with a rusty razor,
Shave his belly with a rusty razor,
Shave his belly with a rusty razor,
Early in the morning.

CHORUS

Some of the shanties described their work. On the halyards, mastheading a yard:

So Handy

Now up aloft from down below.
    HANDY me boys, handy!
Up aloft that yard must go!
    HANDY me boys so handy!
Now one more pull and we'll show her clew!
    HANDY me boys, handy!
Oh, we're the boys that'll put her through!
    HANDY me boys so handy!

Stretching out the luff, or the forward part, of a sail:

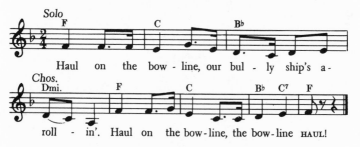

While hauling on the braces, a description of a quick descent to the deck in cold weather:

John Dameray

A loft we all must go - oh! JOHN come down the back - stay. In hail and frost and snow - oh. JOHN come down the back-stay, John DAM - e - ray!

Marching around the capstán to weigh anchor:

Paddy get back, take in the slack!
Heave away your capstan, heave a pawl!

The right song led by the right man at the right moment could double a crew's effort, particularly if the men were in a sullen, angry mood because of some injustice they had suffered—well illustrated in the verses of "Paddy Get Back," the story of an angry crew who had been deliberately misinformed about their ship's destination.

Paddy Get Back

There was a Yankee ship a-laying in the basin.
Shipping master told me she was going to New York!

If I ever get my hands on that shipping master,
I will murder him if it's the last thing that I do!

When the pilot left the ship the captain told us
We were bound around Cape Horn to Callao!

And he said that she was hot and still a-beating,
And the best thing we could do was watch our step.

Now the mate and second mate belonged to Boston,
And the captain hailed from Bangor down in Maine.

The three of them were rough-n'-tumble fighters.
When not fighting amongst themselves they fought with us.

Oh, they called us out one night to reef the tops'ls.
There was belayin' pins a-flying around the deck.

We came on deck and went to set the tops'ls.
Not a man among the bunch could sing a song.

Oh, the mate he grabbed ahold of me by the collar.
"If you don't sing a song I'll break your blasted neck!"

I got up and gave them a verse of "Reuben Ranzo."
Oh, the answer that I got would make you sick.

It was three long months before we got to Callao,
And the ship she was called a floating hell.

We filled up with saltpeter to the hatches,
And then bound back around Cape Horn to Liverpool.

The officers knew the worth of song and put a high
value on a good shantyman, but it could never be forced.
And when seamen refused to sing at all, it was a sure sign
of an unhappy ship. Dana gives a good example of this in
his account of weighing anchor aboard the *Pilgrim* after
the brutal lashing administered by Captain Thompson:

*In no operation can the disposition of a crew be dis-
covered better than in getting under way.*

*Where things are done "with a will," everyone is like
a cat aloft; sails are loosed in an instant; each one lays out
his strength on his handspike, and the windlass goes
briskly round with the loud cry of "Yo heave ho! Heave*

and pawl! Heave hearty ho!" But with us, at this time it was all dragging work. No one went aloft beyond his ordinary gait, and the chain came slowly in over the windlass.

The mate, between the knightheads, exhausted all his official rhetoric in calls of "Heave with a will! . . . Heave, and away!" etc., etc.; but it would not do. Nobody broke his back or his handspike by his efforts.

And when the cat tackle-fall was strung along, and all hands—cook, steward, and all—laid hold, to cat the anchor, instead of the lively song of "Cheerily, men!" in which all hands join in the chorus, we pulled a long, heavy, silent pull and—as sailors say a song is as good as ten men—the anchor came to the cathead pretty slowly. "Give us 'Cheerily!'" said the mate; but there was no "cheerily" for us, and we did without it.

The captain walked the quarter-deck, and said not a word. He must have seen the change, but there was nothing which he could notice officially.

The tone of every ship depended almost entirely on the character of the captain. Thompson ran an unhappy ship, but on happier vessels, especially in the dogwatch and the watch below, Jack found his greatest release in song. Here he could sit back and daydream of love or home. Or he could laugh uproariously at a raucous tale of a sailor's misadventure ashore. Or he might venture to sing his own special song—carefully rehearsed in private moments—and enjoy his shipmates' applause or the way they shouted the choruses with abandon. Anyone who played a musical instrument was in demand; even a tub for a drum added to the concert. And anyone skilled in dancing a sailor's hornpipe or an Irish jig was called on to perform by popular demand.

Susan Broch recalled that, as a six-year-old passenger, she was enthralled with the good spirits aboard the clipper ship *Midnight* during the dogwatch hours, when at sunset

all work was suspended and the crew gathered as they wished about the lower deck. A little girl might mingle with them at that time and be petted to her heart's content. Then she was allowed to visit generally forbidden haunts—go into the carpenter's room amidships to see what new toy he might be shaping for her—look into the galley where the jolly little brown cook reigned, and even peep into his tiny stateroom where his pet hen sat contentedly on her nest at the foot of his bunk.

On bright calm nights a concert was the rule at this hour. Seamen were proverbially fond of and peculiarly susceptible to music of all kinds, from the weird and haunting chanties that seemed to lighten laborious tugging at the ropes, to the manipulation of all sorts of portable instruments.

One sailor played on his "fiddle" all the old jigs and dances, and a joyous young Irishman sang sentimental ditties to the accompaniment of a wheezy accordion, and his tenor solo, with chorus of many deep voices, made harmony not to be despised.

After his first unhappy voyages on the *Surprise* and the *Charmer*, Charles Abbey finally found "a home at sea" aboard the clipper *Henry Brigham*. He gives this gay description of intimate dogwatch sessions:

Every night the 3 boys (self included) & the 3ᵈ mate hold a sort of a "Conversazione" in our "library" & canvass all sorts of subjects under the sun & much fun & many hearty laughs we have at the various jokes & anecdotes thereat related. From talking we go singing & any other thing that pleases us & when in the height of the pile perhaps the bell strikes 8 & instanter every one leaves, some to take their lookout, some to relieve the watch on deck, & some 1 or 2 lucky ones to turn in. Any night at sea a stranger would be surprised at the change in the aspect of affairs between 5 minutes of 8 & 5 minutes after. At the former he might hear, laughing, joking, singing, playing, dancing, almost any thing, but the moment 8 oclock comes every one stops & 5 moments after nothing would be heard but the tread of the officer on the poop & the man at the lookout.

On the second voyage of his career, Charles Low signed on the ship *Toronto.* She was a packet—a ship with routine ports of call—and Low, in less than a year's time, was no longer a ship's boy, but a seaman. For shipmates he had a hearty, singing crowd of

thirty seamen and four ordinaries, no boys. The crew was made up of the hardest kind of men, they were called "hoosiers," working in New Orleans or Mobile during the winter at stowing ships with cotton, and in the summer sailing in the packet ships. They were all good chantey men; that is, they could all sing at their work and were good natured and could work hard, but they did not care much about the officers and would not be humbugged or hazed. Besides this large crew, we had as steerage passen-

gers twenty men from the ship Coromandel, an East India ship that had come home from a two years' voyage, who were going to London on a spree. The steerage passage cost only "fifteen dollars and find themselves [supply their own food]." They were also a jolly set of fellows and when we reefed topsails or made sail they all joined in with us, so that our work was easy and we could reef and hoist all three topsails at once, with a different song for each one. In the dog watch, from six to eight in the evening, they would gather on the forecastle and sing comic songs and negro melodies. There were two or three violins and accordions with them, and the time passed very much more pleasantly than on board the Horatio, where gambling was the order of the day . . .

When a ship was becalmed in the tropics, a captain might fume with impatience over his lost time, but if he was wise, he would not let his irritation crush the enthusiasm of his crew. The captain of the *Henry Brigham* was Abbey's "beau ideal of a Sea Captain"; in warm weather he himself could be heard exclaiming, "Whew, ain't it hot!" and happily agreed to let Abbey and his friends enjoy some mid-ocean swimming:

Saturday Nov. 13th Lat. 11.26 Long——
Dead calm, & Oh——h-how, hotttttt. Not a ripple is on the water & there is scarcely any perceptible swell. The pitch oozes from the seams in the vessels side & your feet scorch through the soles of your shoes as you traverse the decks. I was serving the main togall^{nt} Royal & Skysail backstays on the sunny side of the rigging & well, I

thought I was so burnt & tanned that to be more so was utterly impossible but oh, if ever anybody was mistaken, I was, for at 8 bells every body said, "well you are burnt, for a certainty" & sure enough a looking glass proved the truth of their observations. At 6 o'clock all hands prepared to go in swimming, (notwithstanding the presence of four or five "Pilot fish" the sure precursors of sharks) & overboard we went 10 of us the 1st and 3rd mates included, we swam off some 100 yards from the ship & oh, "how pretty she looked," so long how black & saucy rising & falling with the swell as though she was alive & vexed that there should be no wind to send her on her course. The Capt came up on deck & watched us for some time as we dove for buttons, (you can see one until it is some 100 or 150 feet beneath the surface) the sharks did not make their appearance therefore we infer that there are none around. I saw a very large sunfish today "which boy Bill took for one of the shark species." Oh for a breeze now we have been in the same spot for two days.

When a sailing ship in the tropics crossed the equator, the painful initiation ceremony of green hands who had never crossed the line was also an occasion of great hilarity. Henry Towne, a fourteen-year-old Boston boy on his first voyage, aboard the whaler *Galatea*, in 1815, recounted his experience:

As we were approaching the Equator I was frequently told by the old salts that Father Neptune would call on board the day we crossed the Line, and would come in an Iron Canoe, with Iron paddles. The object of his visit would be to shave all he found on board that had not before visited his territory, leaving me to believe as much or as little of the story as I saw fit . . . At length the day of passing the line came. After dinner, the Capt. commanded those on board who had not crossed the line, the 2nd mate among the rest, to go below in the after stearage, hereby giving old Neptune time to rig himself and come on board. Soon we heard the Capt. hollow out: Back the main topsail. And such a running about on deck pulling and hauling I had seldom heard. By & by a tremendous voice was heard. Ship ahoa. Hollow was the answer. What ship is that where from, & where bound? Galatea from Boston for Calcutta, was the answer. This was intended to represent Old Neptune, at length he was on board and held a long conversation with the Capt. which we distinctly heard though secured below. After giving him a glass of grog and every thing in rediness to commence opperations, we were called up one at a time blindfolded. When my turn came, I was seated on a board across a Pig-pen (which had been previously made water tight and now filled, all of which at this time I was ignorant being blindfolded) after well seated as I said before, they applied to my face a quantity of Greese and tar mixed, and scraped the same partially off with a piece of Iron Hoop, once used as a substitute for soap, the other a Razor. This being done, the board on which I sat was suddenly thrust from under me & into the Pig-pen of water I went, not knowing whether I was in the sea or not, at any rate I got a complete drenching. I was then taken to the pump, where (as they termed it) I was sworn, that is promised never to leave a vessel's pump until she

Old Father Neptune and his Wife

John Forbes

Long by Chron.
30° - 45' West

As seen Nov 22nd 1852 on board
the Clipper Ship John Gilpin of
Boston. My. to San Francisco as
she was Crossing the line.
25 Days out.

was free of water, & not to eat Brown Bread when I could get white, &c. &c. The 2nd mate had determined not to submit to such treatment and had furnished himself with a large stick or club, saying, the first man who lays hands on him, must look out for consequences. But (must I say it) the Capt. interfered and he, poor mate, received his portion of the same treatment, with myself and others. On these occasions a double allowance of grog was served out to the crew, and all labor suspended, this they expected and was seldom disappointed.

John Whidden pointed out that any passengers on board who were liable for the ceremony could buy their way out, either with money or a few bottles of grog. Apparently the unfortunate second mate of the *Galatea* had no such choice.

Whidden describes Neptune and his wife:

Two old grizzled shellbacks were selected from among the crew to act the parts of Neptune and wife. They were painted and decked out in the most fantastic garb, by the crew. They had long, flowing hair and whiskers of rope-yarns and oakum, resembling seaweed, and a crown made from Manila strands and shells, scraps of steel, or iron. Then with the ship's big trumpet, and the five-pronged grains used for catching dolphins or skipjacks, as his trident, his outfit was complete.

If there are any doubts about the attitude of the crew toward all these goings-on, Whidden puts them to rest: "Then followed the lathering and shaving, which was of a pretty rough order, but if the poor fellow opened his mouth to utter a protest, it was instantly filled with a brushful of unsavory lather, amid the delight and jeers of his tormentors."

Another shipboard custom enjoyed by all hands, and at no one's expense, was the sea burial of the "dead horse." When a sailor signed on, he was given a month's wages in advance, which he usually spent before the ship sailed. Thus for the first month at sea he felt he was working for nothing, or "working out the dead horse." At the end of the month, all hands gathered to "bury" the dead horse. This ceremony was described by Captain W. B. Whall, recollecting songs he sang as a young sailor aboard ship in the mid-1800s.

On the last evening of the month, at one bell in the second dog-watch, a lighted procession emerged from the break of the forecastle, a wheeled platform carried the rude figure of a horse made of canvas stuffed with straw, upon which sat one of the boatswain's mates in old clothes and a battered tall hat, waving a long whip. He was dragged along by the men, who sang as they dragged:

Harpoons.

The Dead Horse

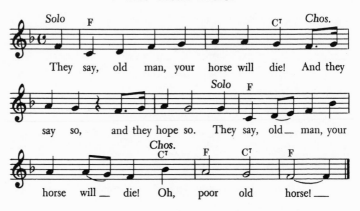

They say, old man, your horse will die! And they say so, and they hope so. They say, old— man, your horse will — die! Oh, poor old horse! —

Then if he dies, I'll tan his hide,
And they say so, and they hope so.
And if he lives, I'll ride him again,
Oh, poor old horse.

On reaching the quarter-deck, the rider dismounted and addressed his steed, thus:

Old horse, old horse, what brought you here
After carrying sand for many a year
From Bantry Bay to Ballywhack,
Where you fell down and broke your back?
Now, after years of such abuse,
They salt you down for sailor's use;
They tan your hide and burn your bones,
And send you off to Davy Jones.

The address ended, the figure was run up to the lee main-yardarm, where a man was ready with a blue light and a knife. Having fired the blue light, he cut away the steed, which fell into the water to the hurrahs of the crew.

Another pastime, during the watch below and on duty, too, in good weather was yarn spinning. When a ship was rolling along in such ideal conditions as to be practically sailing herself, and the mate was running out of tasks to keep the crew occupied, he could always fall back on the "spun yarn winch" to set at least three hands going:

All the "small stuffs" [Dana writes] which are used on board a ship—such as spun yarn, marline, seizing stuff, etc., etc.—are made on board. The owners of a vessel buy up incredible quantities of "old junk," which the sailors unlay after drawing out the yarns, knot them together and roll them up in balls. These "rope yarns" are constantly used for various purposes, but the greater part is manufactured into spun yarn. For this purpose every vessel is furnished with a "spun yarn winch"; which is very simple, consisting of a wheel and spindle. This may be heard constantly going on deck in pleasant weather; and we had employment, during a great part of the time, for three hands in drawing and knotting yarns, and making spun yarn.

On the ships on which Dana sailed, talking was not permitted when seamen were on duty. But most captains were more permissive, and so many good stories were told during the monotonous turnings of the spun yarn winch that the term "spin a yarn" even today, hundreds of miles from the sea, is immediately understood to mean "tell a story."

No, it was not all work. There were many diversions:

*Sailors often saw strange birds, such as this
Atlantic puffin, on lonely coasts and islands.
Unlike the petrel, the puffin was not a strong
enough flier to follow ships.*

reading, fishing, carving, studying navigation if they chose, "speaking ship" in mid-ocean if they got close enough to another vessel, racing her if not, sighting land, shore leave.

But the real bond was the ship herself. Far more than a mere job, she was a way of life, a home for mile upon thousand mile, a living personality who shared the task of bearing goods across the ocean, a partner in the struggle when the elements threatened to swallow up ship, sailor, and all. Without the ship, a sailor could not possibly survive, and without the sailor, neither could she.

Charles Abbey felt this one winter night high on a foreyard in a midnight gale off Cape Horn.

14th [September 1858]

Rugged heavy weather blowing quite stiff
Lat 42° 16' Long cant° say'
The gale increased with the day & at 12^m (night) we were under close reefs. While on the fore yard tricing up the stun sail boom I remarked the beauty of the ships model which in connection with the silver like appearance of the waves (which when combing threw a glare upon the ship equal to the light of a lantern) & the darkness which frequently prevailed made a spectacle unequaled in savage grandeur. As I gazed at the well formed hull & the tapering spars now shorn of almost all their canvass, & watched the awful struggles between the "Brigham" & the waves, I almost believed her alive so finely did she ride over some huge sea whose only errand appeared to be our destruction, seemingly defying their fury, & trying to get free & bound away from the iron grasp with which

we held her in check. Just as I concluded my meditations & began to think I was pretty cold there came a wave which sent our foreyard into the water & I had my fears that all on it would go to & they surely would had we seen many such.

ACROSS THE WESTERN OCEAN

Midwinter in 1851, five years after he had brought his sheets to sea, John Whidden shipped out of New Orleans as third mate aboard the packet *Governor Davis*. His comments about the voyage and cargo are brief but graphic:

We loaded cotton for Liverpool, and returned to Boston with emigrants, some three hundred in the steerage. Very rough weather was experienced on this passage over, and the passengers suffered accordingly. Gale succeeded gale, with a frightful sea, and it was necessary to keep the passengers below, with hatches on, for days at a time. When they were removed the men were sent below with buckets of tar and red hot irons plunged in them to fumigate the hold and between-decks. Two deaths occurred and one passenger had his leg broken by a cask breaking away in a gale. With the record of sixty-eight days from Liverpool, we anchored in Lighthouse Channel, Boston, badly iced up, with crew frost-bitten and thoroughly fagged out.

Walking freight—that was what the sailors called Europe's poor. Many of them were facing starvation and looked to America as a land of promise for a new way of life. And freight they were, packed by the hundreds into the steerage area between decks that all the apprentice boys had known so well, now cleared of the old junk Dana had described.

The passage from Liverpool to Boston cost them $18 to $20, and the steerage passengers usually provided and prepared their own meals. Sanitary facilities were crude, and for light and ventilation they had only the hatches overhead. When these were tightly battened down during stormy weather, as Whidden so tersely put it, "the passengers suffered accordingly." If not sick from the violent motion of the ship, they were nauseated from air befouled by their fellow passengers' wretchedness, not to mention the inability to dispose of wastes until the storm abated. As if this were not enough, the emigrants had to keep close watch over their possessions for fear of the occasional thieving sailor.

But most sailors felt sympathy for their unlucky passengers. Here is a haunting sailors' shanty from the days of the terrible Irish potato famine of 1846–1847, when hundreds of thousands of starving Irish shipped out of Liverpool aboard packets bound for America.

Across the Western Ocean

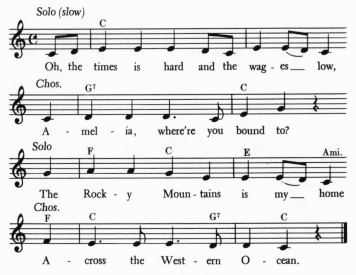

Solo (slow)

Oh, the times is hard and the wag - es — low,

Chos.

A - mel - ia, where're you bound to?

Solo

The Rock - y Moun - tains is my — home

Chos.

A - cross the West - ern O - cean.

There's Liverpool Pat with his tarpaulin hat,
Amelia, where're you bound to?
And Yankee John, the packet rat,
Across the Western Ocean.

Beware those packet ships, I say,
Amelia, where're you bound to?
They'll steal your clothes and stores away
Across the Western Ocean.

Sailing across the Western Ocean, as the Atlantic north of the equator was called then, John Whidden was seeing more of life than most of his landlocked peers. His own hardships must have paled before the agony of the penniless Irish emigrants suffering a winter passage in hopes of a new life in America. As a sympathetic nineteen-year-old, he may have wept for them; but as third mate of a packet ship, he must also have thought of them as a commercial enterprise, human cargo. He was but a small part in the scheme of things, a movement of history, contributing to the development of maritime America.

The Western Ocean had been full of packet traffic ever since the 1820s. After the War of 1812 and the Napoleonic Wars, peace had come at last to both America and Europe. The poor of Europe were caught up by the American dream, for America was just beginning to stir: the West was opening up, and manufacturing was in its infancy. After living for so many years on a subsistence economy, Americans felt money burning in their pockets. European goods, out of reach during the War of 1812, were suddenly available, and Europe itself was about to be available for the price of passenger fare on a packet ship.

The packets that carried all these passengers, and European and American goods too, back and forth across the Atlantic were essentially the same design as any other sailing ship. They just carried on their trade in a different manner.

Most ships were wanderers. Cargoes were bought on speculation by the owners of a vessel and sold at the destination by the captain or an owner's agent called the supercargo (superintendent of cargo). Then the captain or supercargo would buy more goods, fill the hold, and set sail for another port, wherever in his judgment he might make the most profit. There, after disposing of this cargo, he would buy still more goods to be transported to yet another port of his choosing.

Not so the packets, so called because of the packets of mail and papers they carried, which sailed a regular route to the same ports. The cotton cargo Whidden's packet *Governor Davis* carried to Liverpool was consigned there in advance, and it did not belong to the shipowner but to merchants who had paid freight fees for its shipment.

There were many small coastal packets but the big ones were transatlantic vessels—some serving Baltic ports, some the Mediterranean. The most fiercely competitive trade route of all—which burst on the scene in the 1820s—was the New York to Liverpool run.

Liverpool was England's chief port of entry, while New York, linked via the Hudson–Mohawk–Great Lakes route to the new grain fields of the western frontier, was the natural port of supply. Rivalry between shipping companies for the New York–Liverpool trade had begun the moment peace was declared with England in 1815. In 1824, the year before the Erie Canal was completed, import duties collected by the customs house in New York amounted to "within a trifle of ten millions of dollars," and the New York *Evening Post* forecast that "the trade consequent on the navigation of the Grand [Erie] Canal, and the branches connected with it, will in a few years cause the whole of the shores of the North River to be covered with stores and yards for receiving, packing, and shipping our western countries' products to foreign ports."

The early New York–Liverpool packets were astonishingly slow—cumbersome, wall-sided vessels with a top speed of only six to eight knots. It soon became apparent, however, that profits lay not only in carrying capacity, but speed as well—rushing merchants' goods (sometimes perishable) to markets, satisfying passengers who were fretful about long voyages. As transatlantic traffic increased, the demand was pressed for more and faster ships.

In the early days packets sailed only when their holds were full, not on scheduled dates. Delivery of goods already loaded might be delayed for weeks while the vessel awaited more cargo. People were reluctant to book passage because they could not rely on sailing dates.

Then in 1817 a group of New York merchants made a decision destined to bring them fame and fortune: they established the Black Ball Line. It was the only line of packet ships to guarantee regular monthly sailings, full hold or no. In 1818 the first Black Baller, the *Monroe*, sailed out of New York in the teeth of a snowstorm, but on schedule. Her eight first-class passengers, who had each paid $200 for a fare that included bed, board, and wine, were delighted. The idea took hold, and in a short time the Black Ball Line was doing a roaring business.

By 1822 two large ships had been added to the line. Sailings were increased to two a month, on the first and sixteenth. Business was going so well that suddenly every shipping company had to have a line—and the transatlantic race was on.

Some companies, such as Griswold & Coates, kept their old shipping names; others used more poetic names —Red Star Line, Swallowtail Line, Patriotic Line, Dramatic Line; while others, like the Havre Line, preferred geographic designation. The Havre Line, in particular, brought thousands of Swiss and German emigrants to

*The Smith and Dimon shipyard
in New York.*

America from the French port of Le Havre.

The packet lines would continue to depend on cargo for economic survival, but it was the appeal to first-class passenger traffic that inspired the initial competition. Speed, luxurious quarters, and fancy menus were the talk of the town. Each new packet launched brought forth rhapsodic prose from the press. An article in the New York *Evening Post* of April 4, 1826, described the new packet *York:*

> Having entered it, you find the floor covered with a carpet, and the walls (if we may so name them) covered with views of charming American scenery. You descend to the cabin by a handsome flight of steps, with mahogany hand rails. Before you, when you reach the bottom, is a very elegant sideboard, formed of beautiful mahogany, and surrounded by brass railing. In the center is a small library, all the books of which are bound.

The reporter went on at length about the men's cabin, and after an enthusiastic description of the ladies' cabin, summed up with: "The *tout ensemble* of the ladies' cabin is charming and enough of itself to tempt some of our fair readers to take a trip to New York for the pleasure of occupying so elegant an apartment."

The diary of one passenger, John Fowler, who in June 1830 sailed on the *York* from Liverpool to New York, is quite a contrast—in some respects quite similar to the apprentice sailors' early sensations.

> 28th—Crept into my berth about eleven o'clock. Let not the landsman suppose this getting into a comfortable bed

for a night of undisturbed repose; 'tis quite another thing, I assure him; but let him fancy a small room (though called a State Room) some three feet by six and six feet high, in which are placed, one above the other two tolerable-sized kneeding troughs, and he will then have as good an idea as is necessary of a dormitory at sea.

Fowler was distressed by the saggy bed, "a most comfortless hollow into which, of course, you enter, and except when the lurching of the ship throws you for a moment upon the side, must there remain until you turn out altogether." He bemoaned the "incessant dashing of waves close to your head, the noise of the helm, trampling on the deck and many *et ceteras* to break in upon sound slumber." After nine days of an unsettled stomach, Fowler

took breakfast at the cabin table for the first time since coming on board, the smell (stench) of bilge water, now beginning to subside. Fare excellent. Tea, coffee, boiled ham and eggs, anchovies, pickled shad, cold tongue and other meat, bread of the finest American flour, baked fresh every day, biscuits, etc. etc. . . . Our wines and spirits are first rate, champaign especially; ale and London porter equally good, and all supplied unsparingly.

The Black Ball packets held on to their popularity by averaging 23 days for the eastward crossing from New York to Liverpool and 40 days for the westward passage, which was slower because of prevailing westerly winds. One of the Black Ballers, the 614-ton *New York*, made a record eastward passage of 15 days and 16 hours in

1823, while other packets were still averaging 30- to 45-day crossings, and some took as long as 60 days to reach Liverpool harbor and 90 days for the westward passage. Black Ballers became the first choice of merchants and passengers, English as well as American.

But competition was fierce; during the next twenty-five years rival packet captains drove their ships unmercifully—and driving ships meant driving men. Many a packet arrived in port with her masts sprung, sails blown out, rigging torn away, and three or four hands left behind in the Atlantic, swept from the yards by midwinter gales.

Such record-breaking captains as Robert "Bully" Waterman and "Kicking Jack" Williams won the acclaim of the press, and the hatred of their crews. Waterman was a magnificent sailor; it was said that he could rig a coal barge and turn in a fast passage. But to Bully Waterman, men were expendable; he was notorious for his brutality. Ashore he was constantly evading lawsuits brought by outraged sailors. Proud though they were of their part in his record-breaking passages, Waterman's crews did not usually sign up again. On other packets too, sick of overwork, many sailors failed to turn up at sailing time. And woe to the unsuspecting landsman who made the mistake of carousing in a waterfront tavern; he often woke up the next day far out at sea, an "impressed" sailor.

The story of the *Niagra*, which set sail from Liverpool on April 3, 1836, bound for Boston, is a vivid example of some of the packet sailors' hardships. At a court hearing later, a *Niagra* crewman, Samuel Trounce, testified:

I sailed from Liverpool, April 3rd, with one man, WILLIAM SHIELDS, that had come on board for his cloathes, which man they fastened below, and forced from his country, as they do negroes from Africa. The man refused to work—not belonging to the ship. They kept him below in the hold on one biscuit a day and one bottle of water—all the passage.

Trounce's own fate had not been much better. A dispute arose when the captain insisted on keeping all sails full for a fast passage, while Trounce was meantime trying to keep the ship on course. Trounce tells his story, in the beginning, in the third person—until he becomes impassioned:

On the eleventh day out, between 6 and 7 P.M., Samuel Trounce, seaman, went to relieve a man to get his tea. The man told Trounce to steer W.N.W. but the wind had hauled so much to the westward that the ship would not lay to course; and the sails lifted a little, but no more than is usual when steering by the wind. The captain was standing on the windward side, near the mizen rigging, talking with the passengers.

The captain said, "Keep full!"

Trounce replied, "Keep full, sir!"

Trounce still tried to steer the course, and of necessity the sails lifted.

The captain again said, "Keep full!"

Trounce answered as before, "Keep full, sir," and put the helm up.

The captain then looked at the compass, and I said, "She is half a point to leeward of her course."

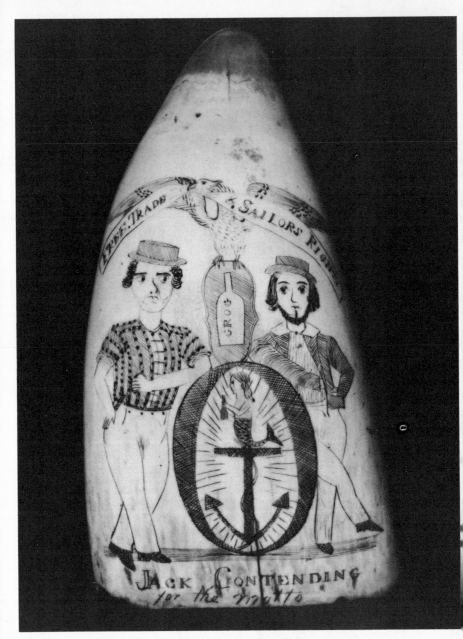

Jack's sentiments are duly recorded on a whale's tooth.

The captain roared out, "Keep the ship on her course, God damn you, will you," and shoved his face as if to bite, and stamped on my feet with all his force, swearing vehemently, "God damn your soul, keep her full!"

Trounce answered, "I will keep her full—but don't stamp on my feet again."

The captain replied, "I'll ring your bloody neck off, God damn you!"

Trounce said, "You will not. Do you think I'm not flesh and blood as well as you?—If you step on my feet again, I'll step on yours."

"Will you?" cried he.

"Yes I will!" said I. "I am no slave, but a free man."

The captain cried out, "By God! I'll stand that from no man. I'll have you flogged, God damn you!" He then called the mate, and ordered me to be relieved . . .

Trounce went below, but when he came on deck with the next watch, the captain collared him. And, Trounce testified,

I also collared him. We both fell. The two mates seized me also and held me down, while the captain trod on my breast and neck until I was black in the face. Then they got seizings on my arms and hauled me up to the main rigging, my two feet off the deck, extended my arms and wrists until my arms were dead.

Later Trounce was put in irons in the hold with the other prisoner,

and so I remained for 27 days in the darkness on a biscuit and a bottle of water per day, until we got to Boston. I asked him to let me clean myself. He said, "No, I was clean enough for such a damned rascal as I was"—and so I was kept in dirt until the day before we came to Boston. When he suffered me to clean myself I was very dirty and had vermin upon me.

In the end, it was not the captain who had to pay, but Trounce, for courts rarely gave credit to a seaman's side of the story: he was sentenced to ten days' imprisonment and a fine.

Not all aggrieved seamen got as far as the courts. For most, the only recourse was to shout out their resentment in shanties like "Blow the Man Down!"

Blow the Man Down!

On a trim Black Ball lin - er I first served me time. Way! Hay! Blow the man down! On a trim Black Ball lin - er I wast - ed me prime, Give me some time to blow the man down!

Now when the big liner's preparing for sea
You'd split your sides laughing such sights you would see.

There's tinkers and tailors, shoemakers and all,
They're all shipped for sailors aboard the Black Ball.

Now when the big liner is leavin' her dock,
All the boys and the girls on the pierhead do flock.

But when the big liner is clear of the land,
The bo'sun he roars out the word of command.

It's quickly lay aft to the break of the poop,
Or I'll help you along with the toe of me boot.

It's larboard and starboard, on deck you will sprawl,
For Kicking Jack Williams commands the Black Ball.

While Trounce's experience was not unique, neither was it typical. A captain did not need to be a bully to get work from seamen. The classic example of the benevolent shipmaster was Captain Nathaniel B. Palmer—Captain Nat, as he was affectionately called—who never raised a hand against his crew. He never even swore at them, but hurled his beaver hat to the quarter-deck and jumped on it in a rage, cursing the elements instead.

Commanding both packets and clippers, Palmer was probably the fairest and best-loved captain of his time, yet he too was known as a driver of ships. True, he made few record passages, chiefly because he would not risk his ships or the lives of his men for glory. But the average speed of his transatlantic passages over the years was brilliant, surpassing that of his contemporary Bully Waterman.

Captain Nat was a shrewd businessman as well, and a remarkable ship designer. Drawing on his keen observation of the many types of vessels he had sailed, he designed four transatlantic packets for Edward Collins'

Dramatic Line, and they outsailed everything in the New York–Liverpool trade. One of them, the thousand-ton *Roscius*, built in 1839, raced the navy's fastest ship, the USS *United States*, and left the huge frigate ten miles astern in a ten-hour run.

With such competition and high profits in the packet trade, shipyards from Baltimore to Eastport, Maine, were alive with activity from the 1830s on, turning out packets as fast as the new lines ordered them. In 1847 the New York *Herald* reported "a perfect mania for ship-building" in that city, where yards were booming for a good mile along the East River. "Lumbermen demand the highest prices for ship timber, and every farmer who has a tree for sale refuses to part with it except at an enormous price."

Boston, with no link to the western grains, could not at first get a payload to support a direct Boston–Liverpool line (England, an industrial country, had no need for New England's manufactures), and the early attempts to establish a line failed. As a result New York was gaining supremacy as America's major Atlantic port.

It was hard for Bostonians to accept this, and they continued to claim their proud city as the nation's major port. Perhaps to a certain degree they were right. Boston had a strong hold on the Oriental trade, as well as trade along the African coast. As for the Atlantic, she continued to flourish with innumerable coastal packets, from those sailing as far as South America to those plying daily commuter routes for Boston businessmen. Furthermore, there were transatlantic ports other than Liverpool: Mediterranean merchants welcomed New England exports.

Clocks, rum, cotton goods, and candles could be exchanged for Mediterranean wines, raisins, olive oil, oranges, and lemons—to say nothing of Smyrna figs and opium brought to the Mediterranean ports by camel caravan for Boston captains to take on to China.

Ralph Waldo Emerson sailed as a passenger on such a Mediterranean voyage. In his journal he commented on the cargo—as well as on his own uncertain state of health at sea.

At Sea, January 2, 1833

Sailed from Boston for Malta, December 25, 1832, in Brig Jasper, Captain Ellis, 236-tons, laden with logwood, mahogany, tobacco, sugar, coffee, beeswax, cheese, etc. A long storm from the second morn of our departure consigned all the five passengers to the irremedial chagrins of the stateroom, to wit, nausea, darkness, unrest, uncleanness, harpy appetite and harpy feeding, the ugly "sound of water in mine ears," anticipations of going to the bottom, and the treasures of the memory.

Emerson also made a note about his Boston captain.

The Captain believes in the superiority of the American to every other countryman. "You will see," he says, "when you get out here how they manage in Europe; they do everything by main strength and ignorance. Four truckmen and four stevedores at Long Wharf [in Boston] will load my brig quicker than a hundred men at any port in the Mediterranean." It seems the Sicilians have tried once or twice to bring their fruit to America in their own bottoms [ships], and made the passage, he says, in one hundred and twenty days.

Boston still managed a Liverpool trade by sending her packets first to New Orleans and Mobile (usually with a load of shoes, cotton goods, etc.), there to take on a cargo of cotton for English mills, and French mills as well. John Whidden took such a voyage as third mate on the ship *Emperor* in 1851, and he has given us his impression of the New Orleans waterfront, full of life and color:

For miles along the banks, or levees, extends the shipping, lying in tiers, loading cotton, staves, or tobacco, but principally cotton. The bales were rolled from the levee by the stevedore's gangs, generally roustabout darkies, up the staging, and tumbled on deck and down the hold, where they were received by gangs of cotton-screwers . . . The bales were placed in tiers, and when they would apparently hold no more, with the aid of planks and powerful cotton-screws, several bales would be driven in where it would appear to a novice impossible to put one.

Four men to a screw constituted a gang, and it was a point of honor to screw as many bales in a ship's hold as could possibly be crammed in, and in some cases even spring the decks upwards, such a power was given by the screw. All this work was accompanied by a song, often improvised and sung by the "chantie" man . . . The chorus would come in with a vim, and every pound in the muscles of the gang would be thrown into the handle-bars of the cotton-screws, and a bale of cotton would be driven in where there appeared to be but a few inches of space.

The songs or "chanties" from hundreds of these gangs of cotton-screwers could be heard all along the river front, day after day, making the levees of New Orleans a lively spot. *As the business of cotton-screwing was dull during the summer months, the majority of the gangs, all being good sailors, shipped on some vessel that was bound to some port in Europe to pass the heated term and escape the "yellow Jack," [yellow fever] which was prevalent at that season.*

At sea, the cotton screwers adapted their wharf-side shanties to shipboard work. So, although Whidden did not take down any of the songs they sang ashore, he did quote a pumping shanty reminiscent of their work at the screws.

Mobile Bay

Was you ev - er down in Mo - bile Bay,
John-ny, come tell us and pump a - way, A-
screw ing cot ton by the day? John ny, come tell us and
pump a - way, Aye, aye, pump a - way,
John-ny, come tell us and pump a - way.

By the 1840s and 1850s the packets had increased in size, speed, and accommodations, so that first-class passengers could enjoy the comfort and luxury of fine hotel living. But steerage conditions remained as miserable as ever—even worse as the tide of emigrants fleeing poverty increased to a veritable flood. Shippers cheerfully packed them into steerage like cattle. Four hundred walking freight were far more profitable than forty first-class passengers, and much less trouble.

Writer Herman Melville sailed as a crewman on one of the emigrant packets, only a few years before Whidden's voyage aboard the *Governor Davis*. In his autobiographical novel *Redburn*, Melville tells of wandering along the foggy Liverpool docks, where he learned how the emigrants were treated before they embarked.

Here it must be mentioned, that owing to the great number of ships sailing to the Yankee ports from Liverpool, the competition among them in obtaining emigrant passengers, who as a cargo are much more remunerative than crates and bales, is exceedingly great; so much so, that some of the agents they employ, do not scruple to deceive the poor applicants for passage with all manner of fables concerning the short space of time, in which their ships make the run across the ocean.

Many of those who embarked at Liverpool were Irish, escaping the potato famine, and all along the waterfront the packet crews were preparing to "stow" them aboard:

We were all now very busy in getting things ready for sea. The cargo had been already stowed in the hold by the stevedores and lumpers from shore; but it became the crew's business to clear away the between-decks, extending from the cabin bulkhead to the forecastle, for the reception of about five hundred emigrants, some of whose boxes were already littering the decks.

To provide for their wants, a far larger supply of water was needed than upon the outward-bound passage. Accordingly, besides the usual number of casks on deck, rows of immense tierces [casks for water] were lashed amid-ships, all along the between-decks, forming a sort of aisle on each side, furnishing access to four rows of bunks —three tiers, one above another—against the ship's sides; two tiers being placed over the tierces of water in the middle. These bunks were rapidly knocked together with coarse planks. They looked more like dog-kennels than anything else; especially as the place was so gloomy and dark; no light coming down except through the fore and after hatchways, both of which were covered with little houses called "booby-hatches." Upon the main-hatches, which were well calked and covered over with heavy tarpaulins, the "passengers'-galley" was solidly lashed down.

This galley was a large open stove, or iron range—made expressly for emigrant ships, wholly unprotected from the weather, and where alone the emigrants are permitted to cook their food while at sea.

With all the cooking to be done over one fire on deck, the emigrants had to take turns preparing their "oatmeal and water boiled into what is sometimes called *mush.*"

It is often very disagreeable work, owing to the pitching of the ship, and the heaving of the spray over the uncovered "galley." Whenever I had the morning watch, from four to eight, I was sure to see some poor fellow crawling up from below about daybreak, and go to groping over the deck after bits of rope-yarn, or tarred canvas, for kindling-stuff. And no sooner would the fire be fairly made, then up came the old women, and men, and children; each armed with an iron pot or saucepan; and invariably a great tumult ensued, as to whose turn to cook came next; sometimes the more quarrelsome would fight, and upset each other's pots and pans.

Once, an English lad came up with a little coffee-pot, which he managed to crowd in between two pans. This done, he went below. Soon after a great strapping Irishman, in knee-breeches and bare calves, made his appearance; and eying the row of things on the fire, asked whose coffee-pot that was; upon being told, he removed it, and put his own in its place; saying something about that individual place belonging to him; and with that, he turned aside.

Not long after, the boy came along again; and seeing his pot removed, made a violent exclamation, and replaced it; which the Irishman no sooner perceived, than he rushed at him, with his fists doubled. The boy snatched up the boiling coffee, and spirted its contents all about the fellow's bare legs; which incontinently began to dance involuntary hornpipes and fandangoes, as a preliminary to giving chase to the boy, who by this time, however, had decamped.

Many similar scenes occurred every day; nor did a single day pass, but scores of the poor people got no chance whatever to do their cooking.

The emigrants had weathered their first night at sea, but it had been a frightening experience. They lay on the crudely prepared bunks between decks, uncertain of what was to come:

No sooner had we fairly gained the expanse of the Irish Sea, and, one by one, lost sight of our thousand consorts, than the weather changed into the most miserable cold, wet, and cheerless days and nights imaginable. The wind was tempestuous, and dead in our teeth; and the hearts of the emigrants fell. Nearly all of them had now hied below, to escape the uncomfortable and perilous decks; and from the two "booby hatches" came the steady hum of a subterranean wailing and weeping. That irresistible wrestler, sea-sickness, had overthrown the stoutest of their number, and the women and children were embracing and sobbing in all the agonies of the poor emigrant's first storm at sea.

The storms did not abate, and the passengers were forced to such extremities that, said Melville, "no wonder fevers and plagues are the result. We had not been at sea one week, when to hold your head down the fore hatchway was like holding it down a suddenly opened cess-pool."

Like the emigrant, the sailor himself saw no improvement in his lot to correspond with the advances in ship size and design and passenger accommodations. In fact, during this period, while wages ashore were on the rise, the sailor's wage dropped back from $15 to $12 a month—for the simple reason that shipping masters had no difficulty in filling out their rosters with British and

Set out from new york. A voyage over the sea, the Cuu, for Liverpool.

Mr. March. Cary. Campbell. Small. S. Campbell. Satchele, Custis, Miller, Heartzog, Crook & lady. Moore & lady. Lawrient. Dr. Attively, Dr. Hosley, & lady. Hephens. Hethrington, Cap: alexander. mr. Ross. Maaree. Chapman. Picabin. Pedrefa. Zabale

new york Bay.

Gone to Europe, Lewis Miller, Alexander Small, and Henry Hertzog, in the year 1840. Gone the 25 day In the Ship Garrick, Captain A. S. Palmer, Bound for Liverpool, the 16. July. Arrive't Save

First-class packet passengers waiting
for a steam tug to put them aboard.

European sailors at this depressed rate. Soon the fore-castles of American merchantmen became all but filled with seamen of other nationalities.

As for the packet crews' fate in Liverpool, according to Melville: "Of all sea-ports in the world, Liverpool perhaps most abounds in all the variety of land-sharks, land-rats, and other vermin, which make the hapless mariner their prey. In the shape of landloards, bar-keepers, clothiers, crimps, and boarding-house loungers, the land-sharks devour him, limb by limb; while the land-rats and mice constantly nibble at his purse." American boys like Low, Whidden, and Abbey were willing to stick it out not only because they loved the sea but because they knew that, as American citizens, they could finally become captains of their own ships.

Finally, no matter how big and fine the new packets might be, a winter storm on the North Atlantic was still a winter storm. Sail must still be shortened and seamen must still expose themselves to the icy blast to accomplish it. Thus when Whidden spoke of the sixty-eight-day winter passage in the *Governor Davis*, "badly iced up, with crew frost-bitten and thoroughly fagged out," he was making an understatement indeed. Often the crews, particularly if they were Liverpool Irish "packet rats" who had pawned all they owned for a wild spree ashore, had to pay a bitter price at sea. "We sailed as we did stand," they sang, meaning with only the clothes upon their backs. A favorite "below-decks" packet song described the sailors shivering aloft near the banks of Newfoundland, where winter waves build up to frightening heights over the underwater plateau, and the Virgin Rock is among the most dreaded navigation hazards in the North Atlantic.

The Banks of Newfoundland

Solo

You ram - blin' boys — of Liv - er - pool, — I'll have — ye's to be - ware, When you ship on a Yan - kee pack - et ship — no dun - ga - rees to wear. But have a mon-key pea jack-et all — read-y at your com-mand, For there blow some cold — nor'- west- ers on — the banks — of New- found-land. We'll rub her down — and scrub her ____ with — hol - y - stone and sand, And we'll bid a - dieu to the

Vir - gin Rock and the banks — of New - found - land!

We had one Jimmy Lynch from Ballynahinch, Mike Murphy and
   Jim Moore,
'Twas in the winter of fifty-three, those boys they suffered sore,
They pawned their clothes in Liverpool and they sailed as they
   did stand,
Never thinking of the cold nor'westers on the banks of New-
   foundland.

CHORUS

We had a lady passenger, Bridget Murphy was her name.
To her I'd promised marriage; on me she had a claim.
She tore up her flannel petticoats and made stockin's for my
   hands,
For she said she couldn't see her true love freeze on the banks
   of Newfoundland.

CHORUS

It's now we're passing the Virgin Rock and stormy winds do
   blow,
With a crowd of sailors on the deck a-shoveling off the snow.
We'll wash her down, we'll scrub her decks with holystone
   and sand,
And we'll bid adieu to the Virgin Rock on the banks of
   Newfoundland!

CHORUS

It's now we're passing Sandy Hook, and the cold winds they
   still blow.
With a tugboat right ahead of us, into New York we'll go.
We'll fill our glasses brimming full, with a jug of rum in hand,
For while we're here, we can't be there, on the banks of New-
   foundland.

CHORUS

But conditions were not always so bad, especially in summertime with fair weather and a generous captain to boot. On one of his transatlantic voyages, John Whidden had the good luck to ship aboard a vessel with a most intriguing cargo.

Some four hundred steerage passengers were taken on board, over three-quarters of whom were women and girls, with ages ranging from seventeen to thirty-seven, a fine lot, mostly French and German, with a sprinkling of Swiss, who were bound to New York, and thence to a western State to work in a factory or mill, on some special line of goods. The run across was most delightful. Quartering winds and a smooth sea produced no seasickness, and having a good band on board amongst the men passengers, Captain Pedrick invited the girls, in the evening, to dance; allowing the crew, mostly Germans and Swedes, to join them from seven to nine P.M. as partners. The ship, having a full poop deck extending to mainmast, afforded splendid facilities for dancing, which was improved by the girls on every opportunity, and the kindness of Captain Pedrick was appreciated by all on board.

THE GATES OF CATHAY

In 1843, four years after he had designed the packet *Roscius* for the Dramatic Line, Captain Nat Palmer was aboard the *Paul Jones* on a return voyage from Canton with a cargo of tea for New York. He was cursing the adverse weather in the China Sea.

Also aboard was passenger William Low (one of Charles Low's older brothers) of A. A. Low & Bro., a rising company in the China trade. Palmer was explaining to him, "On this run you've got seven bands of weather before the Cape of Good Hope—westerlies, horse latitudes [a band of calms] and squalls, then the cursed doldrums, and all the rest. Then the Indian Ocean, and typhoons, then the China Sea, worry and fret, calms and baffling winds—and the monsoon."

Captain Nat proceeded to carve out a half model for a ship that he felt would perform well in all these circumstances. Low listened to Palmer's theories with deep interest, and when the *Paul Jones* arrived in New York, A. A. Low & Bro. decided to build a ship from the model. Six months later she slid down the ways, christened *Houqua* after a Chinese merchant who had befriended the Lows and contributed much to their success in Canton.

So began the tea-clipper era, for speed, always a source of pride for shipowners, was crucial in the tea trade. The first vessel home with the new tea crop always received the highest prices. Thus the swift, graceful clipper was the love child of American pride and the profit motive.

Authorities still cannot agree which vessel was actually the first clipper. The *Houqua*'s claim to that title is questioned by some because of her size: she was smaller than later clippers. She was certainly, however, a striking prototype—long and slender; a knifelike, concave bow; wider, for more cargo capacity than the old Baltimore clippers; slimmer and flatter-bottomed than the Liverpool packets, for more lift and speed.

The perfected design of these fastest of all ships did not spring full-blown from the genius of one man's mind. It evolved from a generation of observations, experiments, and even accidents, but some men played a greater part than others in its development. Of them all Nat Palmer with his *Houqua* was probably the most significant. The New York *Herald* reported of the *Houqua*:

One of the prettiest and most rakish looking packet ships ever built in the civilized world is now to be seen at the foot of Jone's Lane on the East River . . .

We never saw a vessel so perfect in all her parts as this celestial packet. She is about 600 tons in size—as sharp as a cutter—as symmetrical as a yacht—as rakish in her rig as a pirate—and as neat in her deck and cabin arrangements as a lady's boudoir.

Her figure head is a bust of Houqua, and her bows are as sharp as the toes of a pair of Chinese shoes.

Houqua, as he was known throughout the Western world, had been the best-known and best-loved member of the Cohong, a small group of powerful mandarins appointed by the emperor to control all the commerce of China. For many years the emperor had forbidden the *fan kwai* ("foreign devil") to set foot on the Chinese mainland. The only exception was a strip of swampy land along the Pearl River in Canton, where the *fan kwai* were allowed to build hongs—storehouses, showrooms, and living quarters for the representatives of European and American mercantile companies. Among them was Russell & Co., the most influential American trading firm in China, in which Charles Low's brother was a partner.

Prior to 1842, America's trade with China had depended almost entirely on good relations with the Cohong. However, just as the *Houqua* was being built, the situation changed. The cause was the Opium War.

Opium, first brought to China from India by the British, had become almost a national addiction, so much so that the emperor had banned its importation. But the British, in open defiance of him and holding zealously to their profits whatever the cost to the Chinese people, continued the traffic. At last, the emperor acted decisively. In 1839 he sent his imperial high commissioner, Lin Tse-hsii, to put an end to the smuggling. Lin wasted no time: he confiscated $6 million worth of the drug, destroyed it with lime in the Pearl River delta, and drove the British out of Canton.

Houqua—immortalized in the memoirs of his American friends and also in a beautiful ship named in his honor.

In retaliation the British navy shelled the forts at the mouth of the river, and British marines marched inland, killing, laying waste the countryside, and sacking the city of Canton. Unequipped, the Chinese could offer little resistance, and in 1842 they signed the Treaty of Nanking, which opened five new ports to foreigners and gave the island of Hong Kong to the British outright.

Americans had also been involved in the opium trade, but on a small scale and never with the arrogance of the British. As late as 1854 Sara Low, Charles's wife, wrote from Hong Kong to her mother, "I think Hong Kong will certainly be destroyed and all foreigners driven from the place. The Chinese, however, are not bitter against the Americans. It is the English they hate, and they really *hate* them."

Thus, by the time of the *Houqua*'s maiden voyage in 1844, the situation in China had changed radically. There had also been a radical change in the cargoes America was sending to China. Charles Low, sailing as third mate under Captain Nat Palmer on the *Houqua*, noted this:

Times had changed in the short interval [two years] since my coming home in the Horatio. Then the ships went out with almost no cargo but lead and coal, and now our ship [the Houqua] was loaded with pig lead, lumber, cotton sheetings and naval stores, pitch, tar and turpentine. She was so full, there was no between-decks for the sailmaker, carpenter and boys. The boys had to go in the forecastle with the men, and a house over the main hatch was fitted up for the third mate, carpenter and sailmaker.

Cotton goods from American mills was quite a change in cargo from the ginseng and furs Yankee traders of 1783 had swapped for Chinese tea. Far from nibbling around the edges of the British East India Company's near monopoly in the Orient, the Yankee ships were taking over, to the very point of landing tea in London itself. It was largely the rapid development of American manufacturing that gave them their new bargaining power.

Thus it was with a full hold, loaded to the limit of her capacity, that the *Houqua* started on her first voyage.

The ship made a fine passage of seventy-two days to Anjer, where we laid in a stock of chickens, turtles, yams, bananas, oranges and mangusteens . . . After doing this we got under weigh and proceeded up the China Sea and sailed into Hong Kong, eighty-four days from New York— a splendid passage.

Having disposed of her cargo, the *Houqua* put into Whampoa, Canton's deep-water port, and took on tea for New York.

At sea the *Houqua* measured up to all Captain Nat's expectations, gliding through the water at the slightest breath of air in the doldrums and horse latitudes, surviving the fiercest typhoons, threading her way through the dangerous reefs of the Gaspar Straits, outsailing the swift pirate proas that pursued her from the Malay coast.

John Whidden's first sight, and smell, of the Orient was the little village of Anjer, where all ships stopped on their way to and from China, in 1846.

Sailing northerly along the coast from Java Head, the land is high, and covered with dense forests having rich tropical foliage. The ship was well in under the shore, and I thought I could never tire of gazing at it.

About dusk the land breeze came off, sweeping over the ship, laden with the fragrance of tropical fruits and flowers so heavy with perfume as to almost intoxicate the senses. This, mingled with the fresh earthly smell, to which we had so long been strangers, was inhaled in deep draughts . . . With daylight, boats from Anger met us and dropped alongside, while the crews, composed of Malays, scrambled over the rails like cats. They were trading boats laden with tropical fruits: green cocoanuts, bananas, oranges, limes, also vegetables—yams, sweet potatoes, strings of onion and garlic; in short, all vegetables grown in the tropics, with ducks, geese, chickens, fowls, goats, pigs, and many other things, all tempting enough to men who had been deprived of fresh grub as long as we had.

Charles Abbey's first voyage, in 1856, was also to China, but since the big clipper *Surprise* lacked a suitable cargo, she was sailing from New York in ballast to Penang on the Malay Peninsula, to take on a cargo of rice, betel nuts, pepper, rattan, shark fins, and opium. Thus she took the northern route, and Abbey's first landfall was the northern tip of Sumatra, just in time to cheer up an unhappy boy longing to be home.

July 4 Friday This is the "Glorious 4th" in the States but oh how far from that was it with us. It rained all the forenoon, as it never rained before, & then instead of having (as we expected we should) something different for dinner than usual there was nothing but that ("I can't give it a name bad enough") apology for "bean soup." We had an old torn & tattered "Stars & Stripes" at the spanker gaff & the captain & mate tormented the dogs with a few fire crackers, & thus we celebrated the forenoon but in the aft[n] it cleared up beautiful & what made it more enlivening was the cry of "land Ho" from the main truck. . . . & before 4 bells in the first night watch we had "Acheen head" the Northernmost point of Sumatra well on the weather beam.

Like many ships sailing the China route, the swift *Surprise* was soon caught in the doldrums. It took seven days to cover the 320 miles to Penang, an average of less than two miles an hour.

July 6 Sunday A beautiful day with the Northern part of Sumatra on the weather side & in sight. The only thing bad was Lack of wind & we were bracing the yards from starboard to port & back again all day. . . .

July 7 Monday Becalmed all day. In the dog watch I went up on the fore topsail yard & sat down to watch the birds that were tormenting the sharks ahead, & before I came down I had seen all of 20. The water is covered literally with sponges & sunfish & here & there a snake is seen. We are continually passing banana peels cocoa nut shells & various other fruits. The 3[d] mate saw an island ahead & a sail on the Lee bow, from the main topgallant yard. The mate took one of the quarter boats & rowed off around the ship. No course at all.

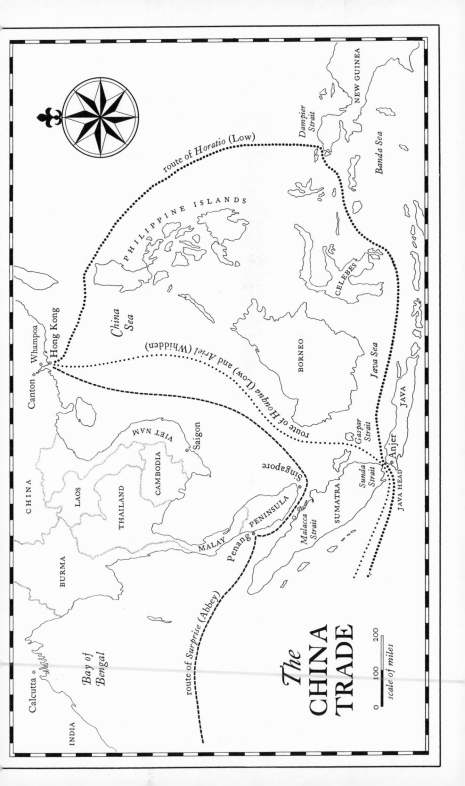

Like Whidden, Abbey was enchanted by the smell of the tropics, which, because of no wind, seemed maddeningly out of reach. "This morning at daybreak," he logged on July 9,

we sighted the island of Porto Penang the long desired place & had the satisfaction of getting becalmed within 6 or 8 miles of it & knocking about all night again. We have been "humbugging" about within 2 days sail of Port for a week. The smell of spices bananas & fruits of all kinds is delicious, & I kept snuffing & snuffing all my lookout to get enough.

When he was finally able to get his hands on the source of these delicious odors, Abbey wasted no words: "July 11 Friday This day we had two bumboats alongside with Bananas Plantains Pineapples &c & I laid into them deep."

But with the exception of two Sundays—one spent curled up with a book and his new pet monkey, the other exploring the island on horseback—Abbey saw nothing but cargo.

July 28 Monday Took out ballast & took in rice all day. I have nothing to do but sit on deck slate in hand & keep tally of the bags as they come in the port.

July 29 Tuesday Tallying rice today.

By Friday he is bored.

August 1 Friday Employed as usual.

August 2 Saturday The old story again.

After a week he is desperate.

August 5 Tuesday Cargo! Cargo! Cargo!

August 6 Wednesday Ditto! Ditto! Ditto!

August 7 Thursday All e same.

It was the middle of August before the *Surprise* was loaded, hatches battened down, and ready to sail: "August 12 Tuesday Got our passengers (who are 12 Chinamen for Macao & an English Missionarys wife & 3 children) aboard, hove short in the forenoon, tripped our anchor & set sail about 4 P.M. The Malay Christmas."

Four weeks later the *Surprise* let go her anchor in the waters of the Pearl River at Whampoa, ten miles below the city of Canton: the gates of Cathay! The far-off city in the dreams of every sea-struck Yankee boy.

The Sunday after their arrival, Abbey and a sailor friend named Bill received permission from the captain to visit the city. Fifteen years earlier such an excursion would have been impossible: then foreigners were not allowed beyond the hongs except for special occasions. But the Opium War had changed this, and the two bumbling American boys had a tolerant reception during their visit to Canton.

First, they hired a sampan.

As soon as safely off we began to bargain with him [Sam, as all Whampoa boatmen were called] to carry us to Canton, and he finally agreed to take us up at once, and bring us down the next night, for the sum of four dollars, we advanced one quarter of the amount as an earnest of our good intentions.

The boat was about twenty feet long, and six feet wide in the middle. Amidships was a permanent, arched, bamboo roof, some three feet high in the center, and under which we reclined and slept with lots of room to spread our legs about and be comfortable. . . .

Except where we sat, she was completely fitted with a movable deck, upon which the crew, consisting of the sampan man, his sons, and his wife, sat and pulled at the oars.

That is—the three men sat and pulled, while the woman stood up on the stern of the boat and pushed at one oar, and steered with another, merely touching it from time to time with her leg.

Just back of our seat was the little "Joss House," or altar, at which they worshipped; a little box, about eighteen inches square, with much gilt paper and tinsel fixtures—inside a small quantity of "chow chow," (food) to appease the Gods appetite, should he wax hungry, and a few tallow dips, about the size of lead pencils and colored red, which were blazing away, while a faint smoke arose from the slowly smouldering "Joss stick," (the "punk" which all American boys use on the 4th of July to light their fire crackers with).

Before this flimsy little arrangement of nothings, this man and his family—for they all lived, ate, drank, and slept, in this boat—were in the daily habit of prostrating themselves, and going through their forms of worship, which they term, "Chin-chining."

With so little awe did the shrine inspire us, that we came near pulling everything out for inspection, before the boatman could explain to us, in his "pidgin English,"

An unknown artist depicts the hongs flying their fan kwai
flags in the place allotted them in Canton.

what it was that we were so unceremoniously investigating; but as soon as we knew, we of course desisted, much to his satisfaction, and betook ourselves to smoking some Manila Cheroots, which he provided from some unseen store in the depths of the boat.

Sitting in their comfortable chairs, the boys were lulled to sleep by the gentle motion of the sampan moving steadily upriver toward Canton. When they awoke they found themselves

surrounded by, I'm afraid to say how many thousand other sampans; on both sides of the river the city lay about us for—we couldn't tell how far, but, to judge from the noises, I should have said, many miles. It was one continual cry, from the mouths of boatmen, coolies, vendors of all descriptions of stuff, children, & dogs, while now and then the melodious bray of some forlorn Jackass, reminded me of an immense well sweep upon a rusty hinge.

Sam set up a basin and towel for them to "perform our ablutions," and his wife gave them "a very fair breakfast, a much fairer one than we knew was cooked for us aboard the ship down the river."

The meal over, we engaged the ever ready and obliging Sam to guide us about and shew us the sights, and stepped across numerous boats to the "jetty" (or wharf) close by, from which we emerged upon a large open quadrangle surrounded by goodly warehouses belonging to foreign residents [the hongs] . . . we passed across the square, up a street, and found ourselves at once in Canton.

They were amazed by the narrowness of the streets, where only two or three could walk abreast; with the eager Bill setting the pace,

off we started up one street, down another, round a corner, thro an alley, up against one man and over against another, dodging coolies with their loads suspended at the ends of a stout stick and the centre resting upon their shoulders, kicking at dogs and staring at everything; talk of crowds why Broadway never knew what it was to have such a jam in proportion to its width.

Abbey's conscience was touched by the politeness of a silk merchant in response to the boys' rough manners:

Sam soon led us into a shop where he said they sold silks and after a few words with an old party in a dark fur edged jacket, silk hose, and small round felt hat, about which his cue was neatly wound, numerous packages of the article were placed before us. We turned them over and admired them, which seemed to please him, altho we told Sam to say that we did not want to buy any. A nice old fellow he seemed to be and one willing to take a little trouble for the amusement of a couple of boys like us, and I could not help drawing a comparison and asking Bill what he supposed they would say at "Stewarts," or "Arnold & Constables," if a couple of Chinese boys should happen in and desire to pull their stock over as we were this mans?

On their way into a temple they were accosted by a crowd of beggars and cripples, to whom they gave alms.

"Such misery and filth," wrote Abbey, appalled by their extreme poverty,

I never before saw; such sores; such deformity; it was awful; and when a mass of living rags, from which there protruded what had once been—but no longer was—a foot, and from whence emanated a moan, which alone estab-ished its claim to humanity, I could bear it no longer but pulled Bill away and hastened through the door into the building.

Inside they found worshippers kneeling before an image of Joss, and again their boatman guide made them ashamed of their irreverence.

In front of the railing, and at different distances away—according to caste we imagined when surveying their clothes, were numerous worshippers bowing and kneeling, clasping their hands together & raising & lowering them, placing their foreheads upon the flagstones of the pave-ment and altogether keeping up a ridiculous "bob-bob-bing" that amused Bill and me to laughter.

This shocked Sam (and us too when we considered it) and he took us through a passage by the altar into a room adorned with plaster casts representing almost every imaginable manner of torture; doubtless placed there that the wicked might see what they had to expect if they did not mend their ways.

After a full day in Canton, they started back down the river toward Whampoa and the *Surprise*. On the way they paused to climb to the top of a tall pagoda where, Abbey confesses, "we found that we had been pre-ceded by so many name-cutting Europeans as to put us to blush, and cause us to leave the place unblemished by our hands."

Despite his disapproval of Europeans defacing the shrine, however, Abbey's companion could not resist a similar impulse: "Bill pulled some plaster out of the cracks and tried to throw [it] into the river beneath us; it was just a trifle more than he could do and contrary to Sams wishes he kept pulling down the mortar and pegging away at the river."

Abbey and Sam became concerned about the angry reaction of some villagers across the pond. The pulling down of the pagoda offended them, and "they began to shout and gesticulate at us, whereat Sam redoubled his efforts to get Bill away, and I seconded him."

But Bill was obsessed with the idea of hitting the river. Soon the villagers, finding shouts and gestures useless, determined to take more active measures: "Ten or twelve betook themselves to a boat and started to cross the pond and get to us."

With a crowd growing and more boats coming, Abbey and Sam deserted Bill and raced down to the safety of the sampan. Realizing his peril at last, Bill too made a run for it, leaping aboard just as the sampan pulled away from shore, "assailed by a shower of sticks, stones, mud and 'Tu-le-ah-ma's' (a native execration) . . ." Once clear of the bank and out of range,

Bill pulled a big piece of mortar from his pocket and holding it between finger and thumb he shook it derisively at them and shouted: "Ha, ha! I said Id throw a piece of the pagoda into the river, and here it goes!" and he tossed it in.

SHIPPED in good order and well-conditioned, by Josiah Dow & Co

on board the Ship called the Silas Richards

whereof Parte is Master, now lying in the Port of

New York, and bound for Canton

To say:

1 Package containing 110 Parish Dollars

J. A. Low
Clark Ship Brittle & Co
Canton

Sold by J. F. SIBELL, N. York

being marked and numbered as in the margin, and are to be delivered in the like order and condition at the Port of Canton (the dangers of the seas only excepted) unto Wd for Spice or to his assigns, One pr cent

he or they paying freight for the said

with   primage and average accustomed.   In witness whereof, the Master or Purser of the said Vessel hath affirmed to 4 Bills of Lading, all of this tenor and date; one of which being accomplished, the others to stand void.

Dated in New York the 24 day of June 183 0.

Witnity unknown   to   B. P. Parte

*They couldn't understand the language of course, but
the action told all, and as we floated away down the current a fruitless volley of stones was rained after us and a
mad howl came over the waters.*

As we know, Charles Abbey had been eager to get back
to New York and quit the sea forever after his unhappy
experiences on the *Surprise*. He transferred to the clipper
ship *Charmer*, which, nearly loaded, was to set sail weeks
before the *Surprise*—and thus missed an event that is
every seaman's pride: a record-breaking passage.

The *Surprise* sailed from Shanghai (700 miles north of
Canton) to New York in eighty-two days, a record that
was to be surpassed only twice: a year later when the
N.B. Palmer, another Low ship, nudged her out by a few
hours, and in 1860 when the *Swordfish* clipped a day off
her time and established the lasting record of eighty-one
days. As it was, the *Surprise* arrived in New York close on
the heels of the *Charmer*.

In comparison, the *Empress of China*, first American
vessel to trade with China, in 1784, had sailed the same
course in about 134 days. By the 1830s some ships were
doing it in 100 days; the *Houqua* made a passage of 90
days.

One of the great satisfactions of being aboard a ship
like the *Surprise* was the excitement of a race. Every man
and boy of the company took pride in being a "flying-fish
sailor" on a record-breaking China clipper. Even in the
midst of his bitter disillusionment with sea life, Abbey
was caught up by the racing fever, when, sailing toward
Canton, the *Surprise* challenged a British ship.

---

*A bill of lading. In the earlier days, ships without a
suitable cargo sometimes traded in Spanish coin.*

June 3 Tuesday I went out on the flying jibboom this morning to loose a couple of jibs & while there espied a sail on the starboard or Lee bow. This was about daylight & as soon as the mate saw her, he commenced to "pile on" sail but much to his & the "Skippers" Chagrin she kept along at an even pace with us & continued to do so all day continually "luffing" & we running free once in a while till about 4 oclock in the aft^n when we were within ¼ of a mile of her. She was the "Skimmer of the Seas" belonging to & from London for "Algoa" bay 600 miles north of the Cape. She is one of the "crack" English craft & is quite celebrated in London for her speed but she got most awfully "Surprised" & beaten too.

Of course, fast passages could not always be counted on, even with the finest of the China clippers; nor were the passages always smooth. There were dangers: Malay pirates, hidden reefs, fire, unknown construction flaws, storms. A captain had to be ready for them.

At twenty-three Charles Low became the youngest clipper captain afloat, in command of his beloved *Houqua,* and on his first voyage as captain he faced one of the most terrifying ordeals of all: typhoon.

Low was elated by the *Houqua's* speed—forty-five days to the Cape of Good Hope and now sailing a swift passage up the Indian Ocean. A sudden drop of the barometer warned of trouble, and the crew shortened sail. Then the *Houqua* began to scud before the storm, as Low described it, "at a fearful rate, and rolling. She first rolled the starboard topmast-stunsail booms under, on both the fore- and main-yards, snapping them short off; she then rolled to port and snapped the port-booms off. The next roll she made took the starboard quarter boat from the davits."

A shift in the wind broached the ship to and ripped the sails one after another out of their gaskets until there was not a square foot of canvas on the yards. Even under bare poles the strain was so great that the cat-head snapped off, the jib-boom went overboard, and the fore- and main-topgallant masts soon followed, carrying the topmast-head with them. Then the mizzen-topgallant-mast broke off.

After a brief lull, during which Low and his sailors cut away some of the wreckage, the typhoon hit again.

I could see the spoondrift, a solid mass twenty or thirty feet high, coming down before the hurricane; and the most fearful gusts of wind hurled themselves upon us. It is impossible to describe the roaring, howling and shrieking of the wind. Never did I or could I imagine it. The stoutest and firmest man in the ship could not stand before any one of the ports, the spoondrift being driven through them with the force of a shot from a cannon.

As the ship rolled completely over on her side, Low's

feet slipped from under me and I fell into the sea to lee-ward, without touching the ship. I rose to see the mizzen rigging just before me, but a big sea came over me and I went down where it was dark. I never expected to see the ship again. I said my last prayer . . .

But luck sailed with Charles Low that furious day. He caught hold of a line and hauled himself up again. Then the crew managed to chop the stays supporting the two remaining masts. These snapped off just above deck, and *the ship righted with her rail above the water. Before the masts were cut away, the rims of the tops were in the water and the deck perpendicular, and the ship was drawing as much water on her side as she did on her keel. If we had been two minutes later in cutting away the masts she would inevitably have foundered.*

For twenty-nine hours they fought the typhoon, pumped the ship dry; and they survived. With a sound vessel under them and a little sleep under their belts, Low and the crew went immediately to work, built a jury-rig, and sailed the *Houqua* 3,500 miles to Hong Kong, where the captain sold his damaged cargo at a profit!

Because Hong Kong lacked skilled labor, the *Houqua*'s crew was faced with the task of re-rigging the ship. "I called them aft," says Low,

and told them what was to be done, and also told them that I would give them grog three times a day, and after the day's work was over they could have liberty to go on shore, but that they must not bring any liquor on board or come on board drunk. They agreed to all and though we were there over three months I never lost one man, nor did I have a drunken man on board among the crew.
. . . They were a splendid lot of sailors.

Captain Nat could be proud of his pupil; he had learned *all* his lessons well.

The China trade was by no means the only Oriental one. American ships landed cargoes in every port of the East-

The Houqua *fighting
for her life in the typhoon
in the Indian Ocean.*

ern world—some of them very strange cargoes indeed. One of the strangest and most successful (it saved Boston's dwindling East India trade from disaster) was ice.

In 1854 John Whidden signed on as first mate aboard the half-clipper *Elizabeth Kimball* for just such a voyage to Calcutta.

Loading ice at Tudor's Wharf, Charlestown, the stores were taken on board, and the crew brought over from Boston, the ship leaving the wharf in tow of a tugboat . . .

At this time the ice business with the Far East was a great trade. Ice was carried out at a low rate of freight, preferably to the ships going in ballast, and bringing high prices when retailed from the ice-houses, it became a complete monopoly and paid big profits.

The idea of ice as a marketable product had been conceived fifty years earlier by a young man named Frederic Tudor, who, despite the derision of his neighbors, had shipped to the West Indies 130 tons of ice from his father's pond in Saugus, Massachusetts. The venture had been a failure and Boston laughed the harder, but as young Tudor said in his journal, "He who gives back at the first repulse and without striking the second blow despairs of success, has never been, is not and never will be a hero in love, war or business."

Tudor was not one to "give back at the first repulse," or the second either, for he finally built up a modest business—only to lose everything in the War of 1812. He persisted, and by 1820 had established himself in the West Indies and several southern U.S. ports as well. Tudor was not filling a need; he had to create it. When sending his first shipment of ice to Rio de Janeiro, Brazil, he instructed the supercargo, "If you can make a commencement for introducing the habit of cold drinks *at the same price as warm* at the ordinary drinking places . . . even if you *give* the ice . . . you will do well."

Tudor was more than a pioneer. For a while he was the entire ice trade, experimenting with different insulations (sawdust was best) and even advising tropical customers in the art of building icehouses.

Others happened on ice as a cargo by pure accident. In the fall of 1820 William Bradstreet's brig *Orion* was caught by an unexpected early freeze in the Kennebec River at Pittston, Maine. When the river broke up in the spring, the crew hauled aboard the ice cakes floating past the brig. Bradstreet's neighbors thought him mad, but he sailed into Baltimore with a full hold and sold the first cargo of Kennebec ice for $700, the start of a prosperous Maine industry.

By 1834 ice was bringing 1¼ cents a pound in Charleston, 2 cents in New Orleans, and 3 cents in Havana. Tudor extended his business to Calcutta, where indignant customers demanded their money back when it melted away. Needless to say, the poverty-striken populace could not afford it, but the wealthy Indians and especially the English took readily to iced drinks—to say nothing of the high-priced apples stored in the sawdust.

Whidden describes a chilly unloading at Calcutta:

Along the water front of the city are great mooring buoys, where the ships lie in tiers of twos and threes. The landings opposite these tiers, running up the bank from

*Cutting ice at Rockland Lake
for the drinks of rajahs and sahibs.*

the river's edge, are called "ghauts." Going into moorings in the inner tier to discharge our ice, a bridge of boats was made, with a plank walk about four feet wide, from the bank to the ship, the ice blocks being hoisted from the hold and lowered over the ship's side upon the heads of three coolies stationed to receive them. It was very hot, and the moment the cold ice water began to trickle down their black backs, they would shiver, and strike a bee line for the ice-house, never stopping until their load was off their heads. During the discharging our ship was a popular resort for all the officers of the surrounding ships, and iced drinks were concocted in every shape. Barrels of apples that were buried in the sawdust in the hold were found when opened at the ice-house to be in good condition, the apples readily bringing from fifty to seventy-five cents each.

All available ponds near Boston were harvested for the ice trade. The thought that ice from his own Walden Pond was to go to the far corners of the earth intrigued Henry David Thoreau, who wrote from his hermitage at Walden, "Thus it appears that the sweltering inhabitants of Charleston and New Orleans, of Madras and Bombay and Calcutta, drink at my well. . . . The pure Walden water is mingled with the sacred water of the Ganges."

John Whidden tells us that for her return voyage from Calcutta, the *Elizabeth Kimball* took on "a cargo of Jute, Saltpetre and Other Products of India." The other products were probably buffalo hides, indigo, linseed, gunny cloth, and—quite uninvited—cockroaches "of enormous size, some of them two and even three inches in length."

Just before rain they would swarm out of the after hatch in clouds, the helmsman being obliged to keep his hat or cap waving to keep them clear from his face, while the decks at night would be almost covered with them, and in stepping on them an explosion would follow with a report similar to the crack of a small pistol. When painting ship they would eat the paint from the plank-sheer and waterways at night, about as fast as it could be put on, seeming to thrive and grow fat on a diet of white lead and "Paris green." Holes were eaten through the plank-sheer, and, on discharging our cargo in New York, we found they had eaten holes in the solid oak bitts between decks into which one could almost insert one's fist. Beyond biting at sleeping Jack's hair and fingernails, which latter they would often gnaw to the quick, they did not trouble us with their carnivorous propensities, but the odor from them was most offensive. Nothing but drowning them out by sinking the ship seems to have any effect in killing them, and that is not always convenient.

When Whidden landed in New York City after one of his Calcutta voyages, he watched as the bales of jute were hoisted out of the ship's hold:

Each one was black with the most enormous roaches, and the instant the bale touched the dock they would scamper in all directions. The ship was lying at the foot of Wall street, and people who had met swarms of them travelling up the street, evidently bound up "on change," came on board to inquire what species of bird they were, never having seen their like before.

So perhaps historian Samuel Eliot Morison's informant was not exaggerating when he said, "An arrival from Calcutta in Boston was sometimes announced by a pack of terrified dogs running up State Street pursued by an army of Calcutta cockroaches!"

CALIFORNIA—O!

Blow, boys, blow, for California—O!
There's plenty of gold,
So I've been told,
On the banks of the Sacramento.

"Sacramento"

The year was 1849. Charles Low had returned in triumph from his ordeal with the typhoon, reconditioned the *Houqua*, and pushed off again for Canton. There letters awaited him telling of an event that was to drastically alter his course.

At this time very exciting reports came from California of the finding of gold, and letters from New York stated that the Samuel Russell on arriving home would probably load for San Francisco. As I was promised command of this ship when I got home, I was very anxious to be loaded and start on my homeward journey.

Six months later Low was off for California with his new command, a beautiful clipper ship. The *Samuel Russell* sailed the 15,000-mile passage around Cape

Horn in a record-breaking 109 days. Low would have made an even faster passage but for his astute business sense. He could not resist loading the ship to the limit.

He [Captain Theodore Palmer] then went on board of the ship and ordered the mate to have all the sails taken out of the fore peak and put in the cabin, to make room for more freight. The mate said, "Captain Low is going in the ship, is he not?" and Captain Palmer said, "Yes, he will take command." The mate said, "I knew it, for if you were going it would not be done, for the ship is loaded now as deep as a sand barge." And she was; her scuppers were not more than a foot out of the water. There was plenty of freight offering, and the ship had a freight list of nearly seventy-five thousand dollars, and a dollar and a half a foot, or sixty dollars a ton, for all she had on board.

Astute the captain was, for prices in California had soared after the discovery of gold on January 24, 1848, at Sutter's mill. Soon, as one observer put it, "Laborers left their work, the tradesmen their shops, the soldiers deserted from the forts and the sailors ran away from the ships." Emigration by sea to California began to burgeon in July and August 1849, and the next year Low turned a $70,000 profit on the cargo he brought to San Francisco.

What a contrast to Dana's unhurried voyage sixteen years earlier in the little *Pilgrim*, loaded with general merchandise to sell to California's then-Mexican population in exchange for hides for New England's shoe factories. She made the passage in 150 days, very respectable time considering her size. Like every California-bound ship she had to round Cape Horn, and although it was November, late spring for the Southern Hemisphere, she ran into the usual fierce Cape Horn weather, aptly described by young Dana:

"All hands ahoy!" was sounded down the fore scuttle and the after hatchway, and hurrying upon deck, we found a large black cloud rolling on toward us from the south-west, and blackening the whole heavens. "Here comes Cape Horn!" said the chief mate; and we had hardly time to haul down and clew up, before it was upon us.

In a few moments, a heavier sea was raised than I had ever seen before, and as it was directly ahead, the little brig, which was no better than a bathing machine, plunged into it, and all the forward part of her was under water: the sea pouring in through the port bows and hawse hole and over the knightheads, threatening to wash everything overboard. In the lee scuppers it was up to a man's waist. We sprung aloft and double reefed the top-sails, and furled all the other sails, and made all snug.

But this would not do; the brig was laboring and strain-ing against the head sea, and the gale was growing worse and worse. At the same time sleet and hail were driving with all fury against us.

Actually the *Pilgrim*'s seven-day battle to round the stormy cape was mild in comparison with Dana's return voyage, when for twenty-five days in midwinter the *Alert* pushed through field ice and around icebergs, against sleet and snow, driven by winds of almost hurricane force.

Sailors sang this doleful shanty as they struggled to fist in the icy canvas:

Cape Horn

Oh I wish to God I'd nev-er been born, To me way ha-y — ho-oh! To drag my car-cass a round Cape Horn A long time a-go. A long time a-go, A long time a-go-oh! I wish to God I'd nev-er been born A long time a-go.

Around Cape Horn in the month of May,
To me way, hay, ho-oh!
Around Cape Horn in the sleet and the spray
A long time ago.

CHORUS

Dana's first California landfall was Santa Barbara, where the *Pilgrim* picked up the company agent; then they sailed to Monterey to dispose of the cargo. The ship became, in effect, a floating general store.

For a week or ten days all was life on board. The people came off to look and to buy—men, women and children; and we were continually going in the boats, carrying goods and passengers—for they have no boats of their own. Everything must dress itself and come aboard and see the new vessel, if it were only to buy a paper of pins.

As Dana says, their cargo was an assorted one:

We had spirits of all kinds (sold by the cask), teas, coffee, sugars, spices, raisins, molasses, hardware, crockery ware, tinware, cutlery, clothing of all kinds, boots and shoes from Lynn, calicoes, and cottons from Lowell, crapes, silks; also shawls, scarfs, necklaces, jewelry and combs for the ladies; furniture; and in fact, everything that can be imagined, from Chinese fireworks to English cart wheels—of which we had a dozen pairs with their iron rims on.

In this manner, sailing from village to village, the *Pilgrim* disposed of her cargo—not an unpleasant occupation. But taking on the cattle hides was another matter. The seamen carried the hides—"doubled lengthwise in the middle, and nearly as stiff as boards"—on their heads, and waded waist-deep through the water to dump them into an open boat held steady against the surf. Dana said that it was awkward work: "I have often been laughed at myself, and joined in laughing at others, pitching themselves down in the sand, trying to swing a large hide upon their heads, or nearly blown over with one in a little gust of wind."

Almost a year went by before Dana finally saw the

little mission village of San Francisco. He was impressed by the great bay.

This large bay, which lies in latitude 37°58″, was discovered by Sir Francis Drake, and by him represented to be (as indeed it is) a magnificent bay, containing several good harbors, great depth of water, and surrounded by a a fertile and finely wooded country.

About thirty miles from the mouth of the bay, and on the southeast side, is a high point upon which the presidio is built. Behind this, is the harbor in which trading vessels anchor, and near it, the mission of San Francisco, and a newly begun settlement, mostly of Yankee Californians, called Yerba Buena.

In 1835 the coastline was wild, and yet it seemed promising. Dana glimpsed San Francisco's destiny when he wrote,

We sailed down this magnificent bay with a light wind . . . we could see small bays, making up into the interior, on every side; large and beautifully wooded islands, and the mouths of several small rivers.

If California ever becomes a prosperous country, this bay will be the center of its prosperity. The abundance of wood and water, the extreme fertility of its shores, the excellence of its climate, which is as near to being perfect as any in the world, and its facilities for navigation, affording the best anchoring grounds in the whole western coast of America, all fit it for a place of great importance; and, indeed, it has attracted much attention, for the settlement of "Yerba Buena," where we lay at anchor, made chiefly by Americans and English, and which bids fair to become the most important trading place on the coast, at this time began to supply traders, Russian ships, and whalers, with their stores of wheat and frijoles.

The tide leaving us, we came to anchor near the mouth of the bay, under a high and beautifully sloping hill, upon which herds of hundreds and hundreds of red deer, and the stag, with his high branching antlers, were bounding about, looking at us for a moment, and then starting off, affrighted at the noises which we made.

This was fifteen years before the Mexican War, but Americans and other foreigners were already gaining control of the local economy.

In Monterey there are a number of English and Americans (English or "Inglés" all are called who speak the English language) who have married Californians, become united to the Catholic church, and acquired considerable property. Having more industry, frugality, and enterprise than the natives they soon get nearly all the trade into their hands. They usually keep shops, in which they retail the goods purchased in larger quantities from our vessels, and also send a good deal into the interior, taking hides in pay, which they again barter with our vessels.

In every town on the coast there are foreigners engaged in this kind of trade, while I recollect but two shops kept by natives.

Cargo brought high prices in California even before the forty-niners came. Although the country abounded in grapes, expensive Boston wines were imported. California hides that had traveled all the way around the

Horn to New England's shoe factories now came back as finished shoes, and brought three or four dollars, a price Dana considered phenomenal.

But the volume of trade was comparatively low, for California was not yet an American port.

Things sell, on an average, at an advance of nearly three hundred percent upon the Boston prices. This is partly owing to the heavy duties which the [Mexican] government, in their wisdom, with the intent, no doubt, of keeping the silver in the country, has laid upon imports. These duties, and the enormous expenses of so long a voyage, keep all merchants but those of heavy capital, from engaging in the trade. Nearly two thirds of all the articles imported into the country from round Cape Horn, for the last six years, have been by the single house of Bryant Sturgis & Co., to whom our vessels belonged and who have a permanent agent on the coast.

Twelve years later California was just as wild and isolated as when Dana had known it. But within a few months its serene rural life was torn asunder. The American government, having won its shabby war with Mexico, forced that nation to cede California to the United States. Within a few days of the signing of the peace treaty, James Marshall discovered a gold nugget at Sutter's sawmill, and a get-rich-quick fever spread across the country. For a few years America was a nation gone mad, and California was the vortex. In 1848 only two ships had called at San Francisco; the next year 742 ships sailed into harbor.

And the rush had just begun. By land and sea, farmers,

laborers, ministers, and merchants were flocking to California. Many organized into mining companies and hired whatever old barge they could ship out on. For them the voyage sometimes took five or six months. To others, frantic with gold fever, time was of the essence; they were willing to pay handsome rates, as much as $1,000, for passage on ships celebrated for their speed.

Cargo was just as profitable as passengers. Goods of every description were in demand, and merchants rushed their wares to San Francisco, turning profits as high as 1000 percent or more: spruce boards shipped from Belfast aboard the *Suliot,* first forty-niner to clear a Maine port, were bought at $10 per 1,000 feet and sold for $300 per 1,000, a profit of 3000 percent.

There was a rush of orders for new clippers, bigger and faster than the *Samuel Russell,* created specifically for the burgeoning California trade. Ship designers Donald McKay, Samuel H. Pook, and John W. Griffiths achieved perfection in their hollow-bowed, flat-floored masterpieces.

Newspapers gave front-page coverage to every launching and headlines for every record. Low's 109-day run to San Francisco did not stand very long. Within three months the *Sea Witch* had nipped 11 days off her time. In another eight months, the *Surprise* carved away another half-day, for a new record of 96½ days. Records were made and broken until 1860, when the *Andrew Jackson* sailed the 15,000-mile course in 89 days—the record established for all time.

Never in nautical history had there been anything like the wild race of the California clippers in the 1850s.

The Best Chance Yet, for

CALIFORNIA!

A Meeting will be held in COHASSET, at the Office of

H. J. TURNER,

On **SATURDAY, January 27th, at 11 O'Clock,** for the purpose of forming a Company, to be called the "South Shore and California Joint Stock Company;" to be composed of **30** Members, and each Member paying **$300.**

COHASSET, JANUARY 24, 1849.

Propeller Power Presses, 142 Washington St., Boston.

The competition for supremacy of the Atlantic in the 1830s and the race for the Orient in the 1840s were mild in comparison. Captains, who might be paid $3,000 for the passage and $5,000 if it was under a hundred days, carried canvas to the limit, driving their ships into staggering Cape Horn seas while crews clung for their lives on steeply angled decks, awash to their armpits, drunk from lack of sleep. Sometimes the captain was lashed to the quarter-deck to keep from going overboard as he oversaw the race against time and nature.

Sailors, who bore the brunt of these incredible passages, hated it and loved it, cursed it and gloried in it. But glory in it as they might, once safely landed in San Francisco it was hard to resist the lure of gold. Many a captain was left stranded without a crew, sometimes even without officers. Before the end of 1849 hundreds of deserted ships clogged San Francisco Harbor; often they were used as homes and warehouses for the rapidly growing city.

Captain Charles Low discovered this to his chagrin one spring day in 1850 when he dropped anchor in the bay.

Captain Macondray told me all about the mining excitement and said that my crew, if not my mates, would all leave for the mines the first chance they could get. I had a fine crew and good officers, and I was loath to have them leave me, so as soon as Captain Macondray and Mr. Watson went on shore, I called all hands aft and told them I was aware that they wished to go to the mines, but that there was no hurry about it, and that if they would discharge the cargo I would pay them the wages they shipped for, and while they worked discharging cargo would allow them five dollars a day, stevedore wages. They could then leave me, if they wanted to, and be in good shape to begin work at the mines.

But with the *Samuel Russell's* cargo discharged, Low had trouble finding a new crew. He was to sail for China to pick up a payload of Oriental goods for the voyage back to New York. He was ready to sail, but

the question was where to get a crew. The shipping officers told me it would be impossible to get sailors to take my ship to China, as sailors were getting one hundred and fifty dollars in gold to go to Honolulu, and I should have to take my chances of getting men there from the whalers, or take Kanakas [Hawaiians]. I had to do this. I shipped fifteen men at that price.

It was Low's bad luck, however, to have one of the many San Francisco fires of the era break out just as his crew was about to board ship.

On the fourteenth of June I went on shore to get my crew on board. I had some eight or ten on the wharf and we were waiting for the rest, when the cry of "Fire!" was raised, and before I had time to turn around my men were gone. I discharged the boatman, and concluded to go myself. The fire started just a little above the wharf at Washington Street and spread at a terrible rate. I had a great many friends in the city, and I helped as much as I could, and worked all day long; but it was of no use, for the fire had the most of the city in its grasp and devoured everything before it.

Once the fire was out, the captain faced the problem of rounding up his crew again. Setting out with two policemen and the shipping officers,

I went to a sailor boarding house, which we found filled with sailors sitting around tables, with piles of gold before them, gambling and drinking. As soon as I made my appearance they sang out, "Hallo, Captain! come and have a drink!" I asked if the crew of the Samuel Russell were there, and they replied, "Oh yes, Cap., we are all here and we are going to stay for the present." And some of them began to blackguard the ship, calling her all sorts of names, and I saw it was time to leave. Sailors in those days had no liking for captains and officers of ships and the policemen advised me to wait awhile. The shipping officers said they would try and find a crew as soon as possible and I did wait until the next day, when I found a crew willing to ship by the run to Honolulu. They wanted one hundred and seventy-five dollars apiece and were to be discharged as soon as the ship was safely anchored at Honolulu. My conscience went against it, but Macondray & Co. advised me to take them while I could get them, so I shipped fifteen very good men and got them on board. On the sixteenth of June we sailed, but I had to pay every man his one hundred and seventy-five dollars in gold before they would go to work getting the anchor. I was glad enough to get away from such a gambling den and be at sea again.

Gold-mad San Francisco was a tempestuous place. As Low described it, "Gambling houses and saloons were all over the city; on the sidewalks you could see tables with piles of gold, and rough miners gambling from morning till night, and inside the saloon from night till morning."

At the same time that Charles Low was having such a worrisome time collecting a crew, John Whidden was one of the young, carefree sailors gleefully taking advantage of this unique situation where it was the sailor who piped the tune while the captain danced.

Little wonder sailors went berserk on arrival. After $12 a month for the privilege of being worked to exhaustion at the risk of life and limb, the San Francisco spree must have been glorious. Here is San Francisco through Whidden's eyes: "One met very few old men in the city streets, but young to middle-aged, full of life, brawn and muscle, eager, and all dominated by one thought, in the wild headlong scramble for wealth: Gold! Gold! Gold!"

Whidden himself was eager for the mines, and asked for news the moment he was ashore.

Wending my way up the hill, I was so fortunate as to meet a "Marbleheader" I knew well, who, after a hearty handshake, informed me that I would find a restaurant just over the hill kept by a townsman, Mr. Benjamin Dixey, adding, "You will find all the 'Marbleheaders' there, and get all the news."

For a few moments after I had entered the restaurant it seemed as if I had struck the old town again. Here I obtained all the news about the mines, who had gone, cost of outfit, what townsmen were in port, and general information upon other matters, then I started for the ship to get my sea chest, which had been left on board.

taking an observation of the Sun

On his way back to the vessel, Whidden was delighted to meet an old schoolmate he had not seen since his first voyage. His friend was working in a dilapidated shack called Delmonico's Hotel. Between them it was agreed that

I should stop there, at the shanty—hotel, I mean. The terms were $50 per week, plenty to eat if one was not too fastidious, and a good bunk to sleep in; what more could one wish? Of course the bar made it a little noisy, and a free fight, now and then, made everything exciting and lively. Although about every man carried a revolver, or some weapon, they were seldom resorted to. Each man knew his opponent was armed, and the drawing of a knife or gun was the signal for a battle to the death, or at least severe wounding. Men would hesitate before being killed or permanently disabled for a small quarrel, and generally settled the matter with fists.

Whidden's hopes of joining the forty-niners were soon dashed. "I worked on shore at odd jobs for a week, but not having money to purchase an outfit, I abandoned the idea of gold-digging." However, he was a sailor, and in San Francisco of those days he had no trouble finding a vessel to ship out on. He sailed aboard the *Eagle*, which was carrying homesteaders to Oregon.

My chum got his discharge, his pay amounting to quite a sum, and we fell in with a Marblehead captain (Captain Hector Dixey), who was in command of a small schooner named Eagle between 80 and 90 tons burthen, that had come out in '49 during the excitement and was then

---

Watercolors from a sailor's log.

owned by Dunbar & Co., merchants in San Francisco. She was bound to Portland, Oregon, with freight and passengers who were going to take up land offered by the United States government. To encourage settlers the government was for a short time giving out grants of 320 acres of land to one person, or if two, 640 acres, as a homestead to all who would settle on it and improve the land. A great many from San Francisco availed themselves of this offer. Picking up another "Marbleheader" (William Swasey), who acted in the capacity of mate, and four others whose acquaintance we had made, one acting as cook, we shipped for a trip to Portland, wages $100 per month. Sailors were hard to get, at this time, even for short trips, and wages ran from $100 to $150 per month, high wages for Jack, but this was more than balanced by the high cost on everything on shore. A sailor, or any one who could turn his hand to anything that came along, although not an expert, could always command high pay; while on shipboard, food costing nothing, $100 a month was very good. Jack in San Francisco, in these days, was a very independent character, who dictated his own terms.

Reaching Oregon, the *Eagle* sailed into the Columbia River. It was sixty years after Captain Gray had discovered the river, but the vicinity was still wild, for the Northwest fur trade had died in the 1830s. "Astoria," writes Whidden, "named for John Jacob Astor of New York, has been until recently the trading post of the old Hudson Bay Fur Company, which had removed to Vancouver's Island. It contained one little frame house, a few log huts, and the fort of the old trading company."

There was a difference, though. As in every area the white man touched, the Indians had been quickly decimated and robbed of their heritage.

The forest extended to the beach. Save a few whites, the inhabitants were Indians, genuine red men of the forest, but fast disappearing before the onward march of civilization.

> "Where swam the squaw's light birch canoe,
> The steamer smokes and raves,
> While city lots are staked and sold,
> Above old Indian graves."

Sickness, diseases of the white man that they knew not how to treat, was decimating their numbers, and our pilot pointed out a neck of land on which he said there were over a thousand Indians only a year before, but now, not one, almost all having been swept off by smallpox and other forms of disease, while those who had not died had moved away from the stricken spot.

Sailing up the Columbia, we passed Coffin Rock on the right. This was a large, flat rock or small island, which was used as a burial place for the Indians. It was covered with canoes, each containing the corpse of an Indian, with his implements of war, bow, arrows, pottery, etc. It had been burnt off by the whites, and the pilot said it would be again, when the Indians would no doubt abandon it as a place for burial.

The site of what was to become the largest city in the Northwest was, unlike San Francisco, still a wilderness.

Entering the mouth of the Willamette, we arrived at Portland City, making fast under the bank.

Portland, at this time, was a city only in name. The site was laid out, but the virgin forests extended nearly to the river's banks, which were from thirty to fifty feet above the stream. The trees had been felled, and the ground cleared for five or six hundred yards back from the river's bank, but the stumps were standing in every direction. There were a dozen or more log houses, no streets, and one small frame building only, which served as a general store for whites and Indians.

True to the venturesome spirit of the forty-niners, John Whidden and his friend decided to try their luck roughing it ashore in Portland:

After landing passengers and freight, the fo'c'sle hands became restless, and having had a difference with Mr. Swasey, the mate, we left in a body, rented a log house, and settled down to enjoy life on shore. I employed, to cook for us, the cook of a barque who had been left on shore sick but had now recovered. We lacked nothing in the food line, for we had laid in a liberal stock of provisions at the store; also guns and ammunition, for the river was alive with game—ducks and geese—and its waters were teeming with fish, the finest salmon being daily speared by the Indians at the falls just above the city.

Here we remained, leading a sort of nomad life, for a month, until, tiring of its monotony, we shipped on the barque Susan Drew, Captain Drew, for "Frisco."

Naturally the young sailors, given the mood of the times, pressured Captain Drew for exorbitant pay. "No

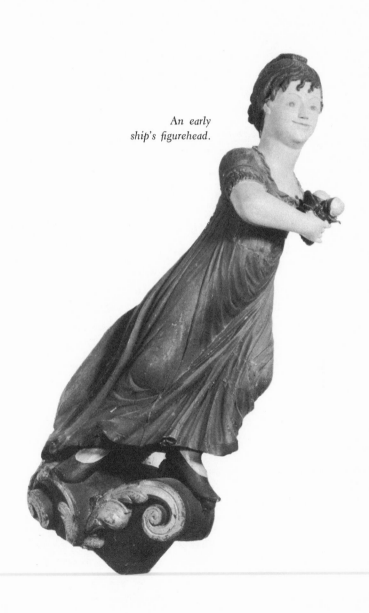

An early ship's figurehead.

men being obtainable in the port for voyage," Whidden writes, "we asked and received two hundred dollars per month, with the contract to discharge the cargo at the same wages. A short, pleasant run brought us again to port in San Francisco."

Whidden hung around busy San Francisco for two months, "most of the time working on board ship in the harbor at big pay." He was still there when, on September 9, 1850,

California was admitted into the Union, the 31st State. It was a gala day, and was celebrated with all the éclat that could be contributed by brass bands, parades, burning of powder, and firing of cannon, with illuminations and fireworks at night. Every one entered into the spirit of the occasion and the whole affair was voted a grand success.

We were now pretty well in funds, and as everything was so high in San Francisco, it was agreed upon by the six of us to take a run to Valparaiso, S.A., have a general good time, as we looked upon it in those days, then return to San Francisco and make a lot more money.

SLAVE RUNNERS

In February 1859 Richard Dana, now forty-four years old, sailed aboard a steamship on a pleasure trip to Havana. Steamers, having made their first appearance in world trade in the heyday of the packets, were now beginning to crowd the "canvasbacks" off the major sea lanes.

What a contrast to his first day aboard the *Pilgrim*, twenty-five years before, was Dana's embarkation on the nosiy, bustling steamer *Cahawba*.

The steamer is to sail at one P.M.; and, by half-past twelve, her decks are full, and the mud and snow of the pier are well trodden by men and horses. Coaches drive down furiously, and nervous passengers put their heads out to see if the steamer is off before her time; and on the decks, and in the gangways, inexperienced passengers run against everybody, and mistake the engineer for the steward, and come up the same stairs they go down, without knowing it. In the dreary snow, the newspaper vendors cry the papers, and the book vendors thrust yellow covers into your face—"Reading for the voyage, sir—five hundred pages, close print!" And that being rejected, they reverse the process of the *Sibyl*—with "Here's another, sir, one thousand pages, double columns." The great beam of the engine moves slowly up and down, and the black hull sways at its fasts.

At sea, too, what a change Dana found from his steerage quarters aboard the *Pilgrim*.

The state-rooms of the "Cahawba," like those of most American sea-going steamers, are built so high above the water that the windows may be open in all but the worst of weather, and good ventilation be ensured. I have a very nice fellow for my room-mate, in the berth under me; but in a state-room, no room-mate is better than the best; so I change my quarters to a state-room further forward, nearer "the eyes of her," which the passengers generally shun, and get one to myself, free from the rattle of the steering gear, while the delightful rise and fall of the bows, and leisurely weather roll and lee roll, cradle and nurse one to sleep.

The routine of the ship, as regards passengers, is this: a cup of coffee, if you desire it, when you turn out; breakfast at eight, lunch at twelve, dinner at three, tea at seven, and lights put out at ten.

On arriving in Havana, Dana found a scene more like that of his youth: the harbor was jammed with sailing vessels of every nation and every description.

What a world of shipping! The masts make a belt of dense forest along the edge of the city, all the ships lying head in to the street, like horses at their mangers; while the vessels at anchor nearly choke up the passage ways to the deeper bays beyond. There are the red and yellow stripes of decayed Spain; the blue, white and red—blood to the fingers' end—of La Grande Nation [France]; the Union crosses of the Royal Commonwealth [England]; the stars and stripes of the Great Republic, and a few flags of Holland and Portugal, of the states of northern Italy, of Brazil, and of the republics of the Spanish Main.

Amid the forest of shipping Dana must have noted a number of sleek little brigs and schooners, race horses of the sea—beautiful to behold, yet sometimes terrible to contemplate: these were often slave ships, many of them flying the Stars and Stripes.

In both Great Britain and the United States the slave trade had long been illegal—America banned it in 1808, Britain in 1833—and both nations had naval squadrons off the coast of Africa to intercept slavers. The swift brigs and schooners could outrun pursuing naval vessels and thus were the choice of slave-ship captains. Their logical port of delivery was Havana: the Spanish still condoned the trade. Every year an estimated 30,000 to 40,000 Africans were landed in Cuba, chiefly to work in the sugar-cane fields. A Cuban newspaper of the era, *Diario de la Marina*, insisted, "The greater part of the vessels engaged in this trade are brigs and schooners, and hardly capable of bringing such an enormous number, even though stowed as tight as herrings . . ." The paper put the figure for the first half of 1858 at 10,000.

During his visit to Cuba, Dana was able to get enough information to make his own estimate of the volume of the slave trade.

I obtained from my host [a wealthy Cuban planter] his views of the economic and industrial situation of the island. He was confident that the number of slaves does not exceed 500,000, to 200,000 free blacks, and 600,000 or 700,000 whites. His argument led him to put the number of slaves as low as he could, yet he estimated it far above that of the census of 1857, which makes it 357,000. But no one regards the census of slaves as correct . . . I find the best opinions put the slaves at 650,000 . . .

A day earlier Dana had observed a sale of Africans not far from Havana.

Mr. ———— is punctual at seven, his son with him, and a man in a suit of white linen, who is the broker employed by Mr. ————. We take a ferry-boat and cross to the Regla; and a few minutes' walk brings us to a small nail factory, where all the workmen are coolies. In the backyard of this factory is a line of low buildings, from which the slaves are brought out to be shown. We had taken up, at the ferry-boat, a small, thin, sharp-faced man, who was the dealer. The slaves are formed in a semicircle, by the dealer and broker. The broker pushed and pulled them about in a coarse, careless manner, worse than the manner of the dealer. I am glad he is not to be their master. Mr. ———— spoke kindly to them. They were fully dressed; and no examination was made except by the eye; and no exhibitions of strength or agility were required, and none of those offensive examinations of which we read so much. What examination had been made or was to be made by the broker, out of my presence, I do not know. The "lot" consisted of about fifty of both sexes and of all ages, some being old and some very young. They were not a valuable lot, and Mr. ———— refused to purchase them all. The dealer offered to separate them. Mr. ——— selected about half of them, and they were set apart. I watched the countenances of all—the taken and the left. It was hard to decipher the character of their emotions. A kind of fixed hopelessness marked the faces of some, listlessness that of others, and others seemed anxious or disappointed, but whether because taken or rejected, it was hard to say.

Dana does not mention the price paid for these Africans, but it was undoubtedly less than would have been paid in the United States. From the time of the embargo in 1808 the value of black slave labor had risen phenomenally; the impact of the cotton gin, invented in 1783, had come to full force, and plantation owners in the new lands to the west, recently cleared for cotton farming, were demanding more slaves. In 1783 an able-bodied slave was sold for perhaps $300; by 1830 the price was nearly $800; and in 1859, when Dana visited Havana, it might be $1,400 to $2,000 for a native-born slave.

Dana estimated a $1,000 purchase price in Havana. Thus, it seemed to slave-ship captains and owners, if the slaves could be brought directly from Africa and landed on American soil, the profit would be very high, especially since the price in Africa had actually dropped. Some have said that in 1860 an African could be purchased from a barracoon, or slave pen, for $8.

Despite the embargo, some slaving vessels had con-

A wooden sea chest from Virginia.

tinued to clear from Yankee ports—during the late years of the trade from New York especially. Ten slavers were known to have fitted out from that harbor in 1858, twelve in 1859. Most followed a triangular route first established during colonial times. American rum and goods went to Africa to be traded for slaves; then the African cargo was brought to Cuba to be exchanged for gold and molasses; then to the United States again, where Yankee distilleries converted the molasses to rum —and the cycle began once more. Other slave ships bypassed the American ports and shuttled back and forth between Cuba and Africa. Still others, though few, would risk illegally "running the embargo"—landing the Africans directly on the southern U.S. coast, usually in Florida, Louisiana, or Georgia.

American sailors, who regarded the slave trade with much contempt, sang as they hauled on the halyards:

> And what do ye think we have for cargo,
> Blow, boys, blow!
> Why, black sheep for to run the embargo!
> Blow, my bully boys, blow!

Many kinds of deceit were used by slave-ship captains to elude the watchful eyes of U.S. customs and port officials, both in clearing from American ports and in landing on the eastern seaboard. The rare slaving runs that succeeded raised afresh in the public mind the burning question of the slave trade. After any such venture newspapers were full of speculations and queries: Will the slave trade be reopened?

There was some sentiment in behalf of this, particularly in the South. Many Southerners felt that the abolition of the slave trade had dealt unfairly with them. In 1854 the governor of South Carolina, John H. Adams, argued, "The Northern policy . . . is to settle our [western] territories as hireling States and to bring them, as such, into the Union more rapidly than the South can introduce slave States . . . They receive annually from four to five hundred thousand European emigrants to swell their numbers while we have not received for fifty years a single negro!" Senator Alexander Stephens, who would later be vice-president of the Confederacy, echoed him in 1858: "Slave states cannot be made without Africans. . . . [My object is] to bring clearly to your mind the great truth that without an increase of African slaves from abroad you may not expect to look for many more slave states."

During the late 1850s there was one slaving venture that became notorious. It was the case of the schooner *Wanderer*, which in 1858 packed into her tiny hold nearly five hundred Africans and landed them, near midnight during a gale, on one of the protected grassy sea islands off the coast of Georgia.

The *Wanderer* had been built in 1857 as a yacht for a wealthy Southern sportsman, who used the vessel for pleasure and racing. In January of the following year, however, she was bought by Captain William Corrie of the New York Yacht Club with the secret intention of making her a slaver. By pretending that the *Wanderer* was a pleasure craft—which to all appearances she was— Corrie planned to slip past the government inspectors in

New York Harbor. The New York *Times*, June 11, 1858, described the schooner:

Her bow is concave, after Steer's model, and her run is so sharp and clean that one would be at a loss to tell where the water would touch it after it passes her midship lines. Her decks, which are of narrow planks, are so scrupulously white that one instinctively looks for a mat on which to wipe his feet on stepping over her rail. The sides of the gangway ladder are ornamented with brasswork repre-senting harps. Portions of the steering apparatus are also made of the same material, the whole being kept perfectly bright. No expense has been spared to make the cabin and staterooms all that could be desired for comfort and luxury. Fourteen hundred dollars were spent in the one item of upholstery; and every other part of the vessel corresponds in elegance and convenience. Her entire cost was $25,000.

It was hard to conceive of the *Wanderer* as a slaver, but she was well known for her speed, and when she suddenly took aboard 15,000 gallons of water, suspicions as to her true purpose were aroused. A revenue cutter, the *Harriet Lane*, intercepted the schooner as she cleared from New York, and the next morning an assistant U.S. district attorney and a marshal went aboard. The *Times* reported that they found

nothing . . . to implicate the vessel in the slave trade. The examination of the lighter's cargo, however, showed that an extraordinary voyage of some kind was being contemplated. There was a quantity of barrels, boxes, bags, and baskets; consisting of beef and pork, hams, vinegar, potatoes, bread, rice, champagne, brandy, and sundry other kinds of liquor in abundance; and olive oil in large quantities; cigars, preserved meats, and condiments—in a word, the most curious melange that was ever seen on board a vessel before; the whole making a year's supplies for an ordinary vessel's crew. There were, it was stated, fourteen large water tanks on board, and there were also three or four others found on board.

In addition, below one of the staterooms was found an armory containing "muskets, pistols, boarding pikes and heavy cutlasses, enough to arm 30 men." But this was not proof enough to detain the *Wanderer*—no handcuffs, no lumber for extra decks, no huge cooking pots— so the vessel was released. From New York she sailed to Charleston, South Carolina, where slaving gear was smuggled aboard. Then the schooner went to Trinidad, and fifty-one days later she was off Cape Padrone Bon, south of the Congo River in Africa.

This was the moment when a slave ship was most vulnerable to the British and American naval squadrons patrolling the African coast. During the loading of the slave cargo, not only was the evidence in view but, at anchor and with sails furled, the slaver was powerless to flee.

With 3,000 miles of coast to patrol, it was no easy feat for the squadrons to spot illegal vessels; however, the squadrons did know the general area of the trade. They knew, for instance, that it was no longer conducted, as it had been during the early years of the century, on Africa's west coast, but had moved southward to the Bight of Benin and even farther south, to the Congo River— which was where the *Wanderer* picked up her cargo.

A squadron officer lamented, "The American African squadron should be largely increased: four, or even five vessels are not enough . . ." He added, "The African station is not popular with navy officers. Not that it is feared—we have no such word as fear in our vocabulary— but because of its expensiveness, the long intervals of 'news from home,' and the monotony of the cruiser's life there." And too, when the squadron was first established, there were so many Southerners among its officers that little was accomplished. One Southern captain, M.C. Perry, reported, "I could not even hear of an American slaving vessel; and I am fully impressed with the belief that there is not one afloat." At the same time a Northern officer, Captain Trenchard, reported at least three hundred slave ships on the coast, and proceeded to capture five of them himself.

As if matters were not difficult enough, U.S. Navy orders permitted seizure only of ships with slaves actually aboard. A fully equipped but not yet loaded slaver could sail freely past the patrols. Then, having secured a cargo of Africans, the Americans could "sell" the ship to a Spaniard by preparing a set of false papers, hoist the Spanish flag, and sail unmolested back past the naval squadron—since the squadron could not legally board foreign vessels. In other cases, if the cargo was aboard and arrest seemed certain, captains were known to mass-drown several hundred Africans, weighted by their irons, to do away with the evidence.

Like most slave ships, however, the *Wanderer* was faster than the vessels in the squadron and could easily outrun them. Somewhere between the Congo River and Benguela, Angola, she took aboard nearly five hundred Africans from French slave pens. Then, on October 11, she was sighted and chased by the American flagship *Vincennes*. A New York *Herald* correspondent aboard the flagship reported, "On the 11th, the day after leaving Ambriz [Angola], we had a chase after a large schooner off Snake Head, under suspicious circumstances. She beat us sailing, however." The same correspondent sent another dispatch from St. Paul de Loando on October 23: "We have just arrived, and learned that the *Wanderer* got off the coast with 350 Negroes. She was the schooner we chased." The *Wanderer* had neared the incredible speed of twenty knots during her escape.

The schooner reached the Georgia coast about six weeks later, where the crew disembarked the Africans on American soil. As isolation and secrecy were paramount, the landing spot chosen was Jekyll Island, one of a chain of islands separated from the Georgia mainland by a few miles of marshland and a shallow bay with a channel three or four feet deep. The heavy surf rolling up the beaches of the island's eastern shore precluded any chance visitors, and tall oaks covered with Spanish moss screened it from passing vessels. Although the island was isolated, it was close to several navigable rivers—and Savannah was only sixty-five miles away.

Jekyll Island was owned by the prominent Dubignon family, and managed by John Dubignon, the only white man there. It was he who made the *Wanderer*'s landing

"The Plantation," painted by an unknown folk artist
in the early nineteenth century.

possible. A week before the schooner's arrival he had placed this advertisement in the Savannah *Daily Morning News:*

Of those Africans who had been landed—a fifth of them did not survive the brutal passage—about 170, mostly young boys, were sent up the Savannah River to a single large plantation. Others were dispersed from Jekyll in smaller groups, and had suffered so during the crossing that they had to be carried. "Not being able to walk," reported the Marion, Georgia, *Commonwealth,*

They were carried in a wagon from the railroad depot to Brown's, and thence by wagon to the St. Nicholas [steamer] . . .

In the party were some five or six men, two or three women, four or five girls, and the rest boys, or what might be called "youngsters." They were each clad in common Kersey pants and roundabout [short jacket] over which they wore a heavy blanket. Women and all were thus dressed. None had shoes, for the reason that they could not walk in them; in fact, they could scarcely walk at all, having been confined and crowded so close on shipboard.

Another observer, who saw the same group, wrote in *Harper's Weekly*, January 8, 1859, that they caused "a great deal of excitement, and the crowds are thronging from all parts to get a sight of them. Meantime fierce discussions are heard on all sides as to the propriety of reopening the slave-trade."

Many rumors began to reach the press, but the affair remained wrapped in confusion. Declared the New York *Herald*, "With reference to the *Wanderer*, if the statements of the Savannah *Republican* and Charleston *News* can be relied upon, slaves have been landed directly from Africa on our own shores. It may turn out, however, that this is not the case, but that the slaver discharged her human cargo in Cuba."

More and more, however, opinion came to be confirmed, and soon the facts about the voyage came to the attention of the U.S. government. On February 25, 1859, the *Wanderer* was seized officially and condemned to be sold at auction. A last look at the contrast between the yachting ruse and the *Wanderer's* eventual purpose was given in *Harper's Weekly*, January 29, 1859.

The Wanderer is well known in New York. She once, I believe, belonged to the yacht club, and was owned by Colonel Johnson. That gentleman was in command of her at the regatta at Brunswick, Georgia, about one year ago. I saw the flag of the New York Yacht Club on board of her this afternoon. She was fitted up as yachts generally, very elegantly. The cabin and the captain's stateroom are very luxurious. Mirrors, satin-wood furniture, damask, and lace curtains, elegant framed engravings, Brussels carpets, a library of costly books, expensive nautical instruments—these form the attractive features of the "yacht." The slave deck, where human beings were packed "spoon fashion," muskets, pistols, boarding-pikes, large water-tanks, all betray the disgusting and horrible nature of the last voyage of the "slaver."

What was the passage like for the Africans? There are no descriptions of the *Wanderer* as she sailed through the unspeakable "middle passage" (the second leg of the traditional triangle), but one can speculate from other accounts. Typically the voyage of a slave ship across the Atlantic was a nightmare of terror, hunger, disease, and—as was true of the *Wanderer*—death. In 1807 the casualty figure for the African captives was given as 17 percent; but by 1840, with the trade illegal and holds packed tighter and tighter for more profits, it was put at 25 percent. The slaver captains cared little; as one Englishman said,

I have known children bought [in Africa] for less corn than would go into one of our hats and you can easily imagine where they are bought so cheaply and where they fetch so large a price on the coast, it pays the slave-dealer to collect as many as he can. It is like sending a large block of ice; you know that a certain amount will melt away but that which remains will be quite sufficient for your wants.

Perhaps the account of an American seaman who unwittingly shipped aboard a slaver gives as true a picture as possible of how the Africans experienced it. In June 1860 the "whaleship" *Thomas Watson* of New London,

Connecticut, set sail for the Azores. These islands were logically the first leg of a whaling voyage, and even the crew had no inkling of the *Thomas Watson's* actual purpose. Edward Manning, a member of the crew, later recounted the voyage:

It was not until after we had done with cruising off the Azore Islands and had taken our departure for other parts, that our suspicions were aroused that the whaling business was merely a blind. The first evidence came to light after the crew had been set to work breaking out the hold, and it appeared in the shape of huge quantities of rice, hard-tack, salt beef, pork, etc., in quantities large enough to feed a regiment for a long time. We also found a great amount of light pine flooring. . . .

For weeks the sham of whaling was carried on, and, whenever a blow was cried out from aloft, all boats were called away. The master of a bona fide whaler could not have been more anxious to secure his fish than our captain appeared to be.

But the sham finally became apparent. A Spanish slave trader, or "palm oil merchant" as Manning calls him, was contacted, plans made, and a landing boat sighted and signaled. The *Thomas Watson* started toward the beach and anchored

dangerously near the breakers. The sails were allowed to hang in the buntlines, not half hauled up, and even the royals did not have the turn of a gasket around them. It was surprising that the ship did not drag her anchor, with so much sail for the wind to act on. She lay hard aback, and kept the small scope of chain out as taut as a harp-string.

"Let everything hang as it is," sung out the captain to the mate, "and send all hands into the hold to put down the flooring. Don't be particular, but bear a hand."

Once the flooring was in place Manning and his shipmates "tumbled into our boats and shoved clear of the ship." They rowed to the beach.

Five or six strokes more would have put us in the breakers, when the order was given to lie on our oars. Looking toward the barracoon, I saw a long line of negroes walking, in single file, toward the beach, where a surfboat was ready for launching. After a number of them had gathered around the boat she was shoved out far enough to float, the crew standing in the water up to their waists, and holding fast to the gunwales on each side, in order to keep her bow to the breakers. The negroes were then seized, one by one, and tumbled in promiscuously. After loading her full, the crew jumped in and seized the paddles.

The surfboat was launched skillfully through the breakers despite the violence of the sea.

The mate now gave us orders to receive the negroes and carry them to the ship. He cautioned us to take in our oars the moment the surf-boat reached us, and then to seize the paddles and stand ready to knock the negroes over the head if they should all attempt to jump into our boat at once.

This warning was timely, for no sooner had she gained

our side than the rush began. We did our best to keep them back by using the only argument they could understand, namely, hard knocks over the head. We were nearly swamped, nevertheless, by a number of them getting on one side of our boat as they piled into her. After they were all in we shipped the oars and started for our vessel, the surf-boat returning to the beach for another load. We made slow progress, the boat being so overloaded that it was impossible to take a fair stroke without chafing the backs of the negroes or striking them in the face with the oars.

When we finally reached the ship they were passed up the ladder until they came within the grasp of two swarthy Portuguese, stationed in the gangway. These men, who had come from the shore in the first boat, hauled the negroes upon deck. The poor creatures were much scratched and bruised by this rough handling.

Back and forth they went, brutally loading their unhappy cargo aboard. Then Manning and his mates returned to the ship.

When we arrived on board everything was in confusion. The negroes had been put into the hold without the least regard for stowage. Consequently, they were literally piled on one another; and the unsteady motion of the ship, combined with the foul air and great heat, made the place simply horrible. Naturally, they were nearly all dreadfully sick at the stomach.

After a frantic effort to get the *Thomas Watson* moving—she was almost blown back into the surf—the crew

Some slaves were quartered between decks, a luxury compared with their companions' condition in the hold.

finally fought clear of land and headed for the open sea. "Early next morning," says Manning,

preparations were made to get a meal ready for the negroes. One of the try-pots [cooking pots] was filled about three-quarters full of rice, and two of the most intelligent of the blacks were appointed cooks, the cooper acting as superintendent. While this was being done we went down into the hold to see how they had fared during the dreadful night that had just passed. Their haggard looks bore evidence of the misery they had undergone. Pent up in such close quarters, and inhaling such a terrible stench, it was miraculous that one-half of them had not perished. We found five or six dead bodies, which were at once hoisted to the deck and consigned to the deep. There was no pretense of any religious ceremony. Just as they were, naked and forlorn, they were tossed overboard, and for a long time we could see the bodies floating in the wake of the ship. I could not stay below long, for the stench almost suffocated me. On reaching the deck I heard the captain say that at eight bells the negroes must all be ordered up on deck to mess, and while they were thus employed we should thoroughly cleanse the hold.

Even with the best use of the limited space on the ship, the slaves were miserably uncomfortable. Krumen, natives who were skilled as boatmen, shepherded them into the hold.

On the first day, when we had finished feeding them in the afternoon, it was six o'clock, the time appointed for all the negroes to be stowed away for the night. After the deck was cleared we went below to see that the Kroomen arranged them properly. Commencing forward, we made the first man lie down, head to windward, facing toward the bow, and the knees slightly drawn toward the chin. Another one was then placed alongside, with his breast touching the back of the first, and his knees bent at a similar angle. In this manner we stowed them, in tiers, the length and width of the hold. The Kroomen were allowed the privilege of reclining as they chose, but it was their duty to keep the others in their proper places. When daylight came the negroes could change their positions to suit themselves.

Many of the Africans, Manning observed, faced their suffering and degradation with a demonstration of courage and pride.

One morning a Krooman reported to the Spanish captain a negro who had resisted his authority during the night. The offender was hustled upon deck, stretched out at full length, face downward, and tied to the ring-bolts. One of the Kroomen now commenced lashing the poor creature over the back, and when he flagged another took his place and renewed the beating. The negro was grit to the bone, and made not the slightest outcry. Not until life was almost extinct did the Spaniard order him released.

Other blacks hid the depths of their despair, then tried to commit suicide at the first opportunity.

There was a large and corpulent woman in the steerage, whom the sailors called "Miss Porpoise," and, judging by the grin that was always on her countenance, she seemed to be happy and contented with her present quarters. One day she appeared anxious to look over the rail, and to gratify her desire someone gave her permission to do so. I was suddenly startled by the shrill cries of a female and on looking aft I saw the Spaniard lambasting Miss Porpoise. He was holding her by the wool with his left hand, and she was bawling at a tremendous rate. After he had given her a sound thrashing a nail was driven into one of the beams in the steerage, when a piece of ordinary twine was tied around Miss Porpoise's arm and secured to the nail.

It afterward transpired that this excitement was caused by "Miss Porpoise" trying to jump overboard. She nearly succeeded, as her body was half-way over the rail before the Spaniard saw her, and he was just in time to seize her legs and haul her back. We watched her after this, but she never broke the twine by which her arm was held. It was not a very secure way of putting her in irons, but it nevertheless answered the purpose.

By contrast to the African captives' dignity and pride, the white master of the *Thomas Watson* was merciless. For several nights one Negro, through a clever device, had been stealing extra water for himself and his fellows, since they were allowed only a pint a day. Finally caught, he refused to implicate any of his compatriots.

The culprit was now brought before him, when he gave orders to the Kroomen to lash him to the ring-bolts in the deck. After securing the poor wretch so that it would be impossible for him to move a limb, the order was given to the Kroomen to proceed to business. This they did by beating him with their whips, putting forth all their strength in delivering the blows. The punishment continued so long that I thought the man would have died under it; but his endurance was wonderful, and he only uttered a few groans.

THERE SHE BLOWS

And now that he is ours, my boys,
We'll tow him alongside
And over with our blubber hooks
To rob him of his hide.

"Blow Ye Winds"

This morning the men were up as soon as they could see to work, cutting in the whale. I went up on deck when they were hoisting the head up. . . . My husband wanted me to walk into the whale's mouth. He pushed me in a little ways so I think I can say I have been inside of a whale's mouth. Six or eight people could go in and sit down at one time. . . .

These fish are truly one of the wonderful works of God, and well may we think that everything in the deep is wonderful.

Eliza Azelia Williams was filled with wonder at all she saw on this, her first voyage aboard her husband's whaleship *Florida* in 1858. The crew had just harpooned its first whale, and before the end of the next three long years at sea, Eliza Williams was to see many more won-ders—and go to the very extremities of the earth.

It had been a hard choice for a woman to make: home in Wethersfield, Connecticut, with two young children and relatives, surrounded by friends and with the good earth to walk upon—or the sea with her captain husband, a life isolated, and except for occasional landfalls, con-fined to a small ship.

Most women chose the hearthfire, but a remarkable number of captains' wives did go to sea, not only on whaleships but on merchantmen as well. Charles Low and John Whidden sailed many voyages with their wives. Whidden explained,

A captain's position on shipboard at sea is a peculiar one. . . . All on board, except himself, have com-panions . . .

So, I believe, if the captain is married, and his wife is in good health, enjoys travel, and is not afraid of the water, it were better she should accompany her husband on his voyages as one to whom he can always turn for companionship and confidences at sea.

Woman's influence on shipboard, if she is a true, good woman, is felt for good throughout the ship. She has a refining influence, and the sailors guard their words and actions more in her presence, for no sailor, old or young, would pain her by thought or deed. How often have I seen Jack's face brighten up, when "the old woman" spoke a few pleasant, kindly words to him! No matter how young the captain and his wife may be, they are always to the sailors on shipboard "the old man" and "the old woman." *It is a habit they have, with no desire to be flippant or disrespectful.*

A number of the captains' wives who went to sea kept diaries, and so did Eliza Williams. She began it the day the *Florida* sailed out of Fairhaven, Massachusetts, calling it "Journal of a Whaling Voyage to the Indian and Pacific Oceans, Kept on Board the Ship Florida, T. W. Williams, Master, Commencing September 7th 1858." An early entry reflected her last thoughts about the home she was leaving: "There we have left Dear Friends, Parents, and Children, Brothers and Sisters, all near and dear to us. But I will drop the subject; it is too gloomy to contemplate, and return to the Ship."

The *Florida*, lying off ahead as Eliza approached it by steamer tug, had been built in 1821 originally as a Liverpool packet. Thus she was bigger and faster than most whalers: 522 tons and 123 feet long. The *Florida* was a "five-boat ship," which meant that she carried three thirty-foot whaleboats on the larboard side and two on the starboard side—the remaining space to starboard being reserved for the cutting stage, or platform, where whales were hauled alongside for "cutting in."

Soon after Eliza Williams boarded the *Florida*, she took a long last look at the land:

There is no wind and the Tug Steamer is towing us along. Mr. Fish has just given me the glass to look at the points of interest; there are not many now. The one of the greatest interest I think we have left behind; that of New Bedford. It looks beautiful from the water.

New Bedford, just across Fall River from her little sister port of Fairhaven, was now undisputedly the world's whaling capital, in her peak year of 1857 keeping over 10,000 men busy each day fitting out for departures and heralding the return of hundreds of ships who claimed her as home port. Nantucket, the little island only fifteen miles long and five miles wide, whose history had begun in the days of offshore whalermen, had at last surrendered supremacy to New Bedford. As larger ships were built to make the long three- to four-year whaling voyages more profitable, it became more and more difficult for them to negotiate the sandbar across Nantucket's harbor. Even the "camel," a huge floating drydock built in 1842 to float larger vessels over the bar, failed to rescue the island from decline.

Whaling was an established industry in many coastal towns: Stonington, Mystic, and New London in Connecticut; Sag Harbor on Long Island; Edgartown and Provincetown on Martha's Vineyard; and Gloucester and New Bedford in Massachusetts. By 1847 American whalers numbered 735 out of the total world fleet of 965. Over 30 percent of each year's American catch went for export at handsome profits, while at home whale oil was the only smokeless and odorless fuel available. Petroleum had not yet been discovered, and the demand for whale oil had increased enormously: to lubricate machinery; to light homes, public buildings, and city streets. Almost as valuable was whalebone, especially baleen, long thin bones with great elasticity that were ideal for ladies' corsets.

So with any kind of fisherman's luck, the *Florida*'s voyage should be a profitable one. On an average three years out, the *Florida* could expect to take 1,500 to 2,000 barrels of oil (a barrel held 31½ gallons) worth about $1.20 a gallon, and 45,000 pounds of bone worth 45¢ a pound—in all about $85,000 worth of oil and bone. With expenses paid, some $60,000 to $70,000 in profits would be divided up among the owners and crew, each one getting a fractional part called a lay.

Captain Williams, with his one-twelfth lay, would earn $5,000 or $6,000, and the average sailor, with a 1/180 lay, would realize $300 to $400, about what a seaman would earn over a three-year period on a merchant ship. With very good luck, they could more than double that amount, or with poor luck they might barely make expenses. For example, in the book containing the settlements of the voyage of the whaleship *Milton* ending in 1844 is a copy of a receipt signed by John Murray, ordinary seaman:

New Bedford 5m25, 1844 Received of Henry Taber & Co. ten cents balance due me for my late voyage in Ship Milton and also Ten dollars in cash and for which I release said Ship Capt Lewis and officers from all claims & demands.

his
John X Murray
mark

The *Florida* set out September 7, 1858, sailing through the sperm whale grounds of the Atlantic—touching at Brava, Trinidad, and Tristan de Cunha—toward the Cape of Good Hope. Like anyone new to the sea, Eliza was sick for the first week. As a housewife accustomed to a long day's work, she felt self-conscious about her inactivity. On September 15 she wrote:

> *Such a busy lot of Men. It seems to me like a good many work Shops combined; Coopers, Carpenters, Blacksmith, and sail-makers, they are all to work at something. It makes me think that I am lazy; I have not done much yet but look on. I have seen them tack Ship. That is some excitement, the Officers giveing orders, the Men trying to obey them, but they have not learned the ropes all yet and they make a good many mistakes, though they are all called by name. I am afraid I should be a dull scholar at learning them.*

Eliza's comment that "they have not learned the ropes all yet" reveals the difficulty whaleships encountered hiring sailors. Because of the length of whaling voyages, experienced hands were hard to get. Seventeen members of the *Florida*'s crew signed on as green hands, many of them farm boys seeking a more adventurous life; five regretted it enough to desert ship before the voyage was over.

Two days later Eliza felt well enough to make herself useful. "September 17th. Another fine day; the wind is not verry fair. Have sowed a little for the first time, helped my Husband make a sail for his boat."

She was pleased to see that Sunday at sea was properly observed aboard her husband's ship.

> *September 19th. Fair wind. It is the Sabbath, and all is orderly and quiet on board; much more so than I expected among so many Men between 30 and 40. All*

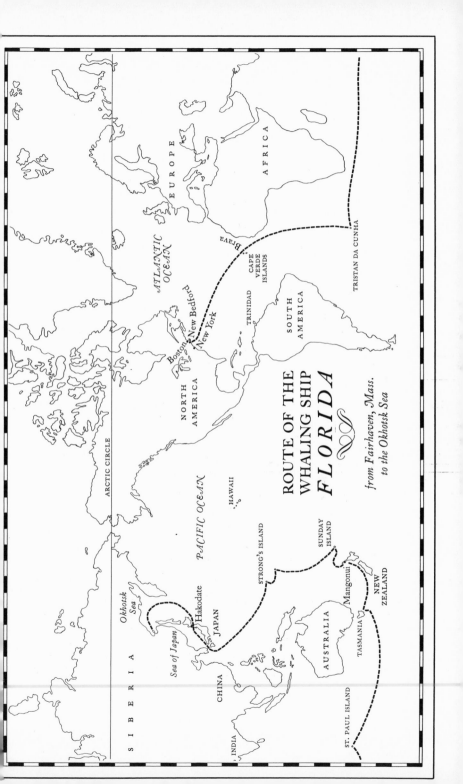

ROUTE OF THE
WHALING SHIP
FLORIDA

*from Fairhaven, Mass.
to the Okhotsk Sea*

work is laid aside Saturday night and nothing done on Sunday but what is necessary. 3 Ships in sight this morning, from mast head.

As far as the business of catching whales was concerned, the voyage was off to a fairly encouraging start. Two days out the *Florida* caught some blackfish—whales that are very small, but render a high-quality oil. Three weeks out they took a sperm calf, which rendered nine barrels of oil, worth roughly $340. A month went by before they sighted another whale, but as Eliza said, he "was an old fellow, I guess, for he seemed too cunning for them."

A week later, on November 8 and only two months out, their luck really turned. The *Florida* was at a point in the South Atlantic midway between Africa and South America, about 800 miles north of the Cape of Good Hope. First they sighted and took a forty-barrel sperm whale. Then the following day,

November 9th. A fine morning, with a gentle breeze. My Husband has kept the Ship off through the night thinking there might be a school of sperm whales about here, and it happened quite lucky that he did, for about 9 o'clock there was a cry of sperm whales.

The lookout, a position manned on a whaler from dawn to dusk far above the deck at the masthead, had seen the spout—vapor blown high from the blowhole of a surfacing whale exhaling breath after a long underwater search for food. With the cry "There blows," the entire ship's company burst into action. Six men tumbled into each of the whaleboats hanging on davits over the water, already laden with oars, sails, emergency supplies, lances, and irons (harpoons). First three boats were lowered for the chase, which went on all morning, then:

After dinner the third Mate lowered his boat, for about that time there was a great number seen in another direction. There were 4 boats off chasing those whales. I watched them through the glass all the afternoon. Some of the time I could not see the boats with the naked eye. . . . Though they were a good way off, we could tell when the iron was thrown for the whale spouted blood and we could see it plain. In a short time they seemed to be all around them. We could see them spouting all around. I should think there were more than a hundred. It was quite an exciting scene to me and mixed with a good deal of fear for the safety of those Men. It seemed to me they were under the boats and every plunge would dash them in pieces. The Men on the Ship seemed to enjoy the fun, for they would shout and laugh; every time the whale spouted near the boat, they thought they were fast to one.

When the harpoon was fast, the frightened and angry whale would usually sound—dive straight down—and the line would shriek as it burned around the loggerhead and through the chock on the bow. Or if the whale did not sound, as Eliza observed, "it takes the boat along with great rapidity," for what the whalermen called a Nantucket sleigh ride.

Presently the first Mate came alongside with one, a cow whale. They are not as large as the males. This one,

*Mother ship, whaleboats, and whales,
as seen by a sailor who etched
the scene on a whale's tooth.*

the Mate told me, had a very small calf. I must say I was sorry to hear it. The poor little thing could not keep up with the rest, the mother would not leave it and lost her life. He says they exhibit the most affection for their young of any dumb animal he ever saw. This one had a number of scars from fighting.

It was fast getting night, but in a short time my Husband's [boat] returned. They had also taken one. They were made fast to the Ship, and two boats sent to the assistance of the other two that were now so far off that I could not see them. It was getting quite duskish, too. One of them, the Men knew, had got a whale, but the other one they did not know anything about. It got dark and they had no lanterns in their boats. The Men built a fire on the try works, of bits of tarred rope and scraps, which made a nice blaze. They also hung lanterns in the rigging. They halloaed to them and got the horn and blew. My Husband told me he was not alarmed about them, for it was calm and they could keep track of the Ship. . . . All anxiety was at an end in a short time, by the little boats answering to the call of the Ship. Soon they came back, all of them, and the two that were away had each of them a large whale. I was glad when they came for I was fearful of their safety, and the quiet of the Ship before, with the fire and the occasional halloaing and blowing of the horn, made it appear an awful, solemn time to me, not being acquainted with such scenes.

The 4 whales are made fast till morning, the Men are all highly pleased with their day's work and are now ready for their supper, hungry and tired enough I think.

The following morning, as the crew began to cut in the whales, Eliza climbed into her husband's boat hanging in its davits "to have a good chance to see them and be out of the way at the same time."

It must be quite an art [she observed], as well as a good deal of work to cut in the whale. He is all the time lying on the surface of the water as they work at him. He is made secure in the position they want him, at first, lying close alongside of the Ship. A Man goes right down on his back, and hooks a large stout hook into a rope that is made fast to his jaw. This is made fast up aloft by means of ropes and tackles. They have two stagings let down at the side of the Ship. The Men go down and stand on these, with their long spades, and cut. They seem to know exactly where to cut. They begin to cut a great strip. The hook is put through a hole that is cut in the end of this piece by the boarding knife. Then it is drawn up by the tackle as it is cut. They do not stop till the piece goes clear around. Then it comes clear up and is let down into the blubber room where it is afterwards cut in pieces suitable for the mincing machine. They keep cutting in that way till it is all off; even the flukes and fins have a good deal of fat on them. The head they cut off and take on board in the same way that the rest is. It was singular to me to see how well they could part the head from the body and find the joint so nicely. When it came on deck, it was such a large head, it swung against the side of the Ship till it seemed to me to shake with the weight of it.

From the head came valuable spermacetti, used for making fine odorless candles, and the even more valuable "case," a basin of pure oil in the center of the head. "They yield a sight of oil," said Eliza. And she noted, "The Men saved the jawbones—I suppose they intend to make something fancy from them when there is leisure. They only save the bone out of the head. It is white out of the sperm whale and black out of the other kinds."

Cutting in the whales continued "till night and all night too." The business had to be done immediately. Sharks took a great toll; furthermore, should a sudden storm arise, the *Florida* might be forced to abandon the whales—or have their huge bulk batter the ship to pieces. Thus when bad weather threatened, the *Florida*'s crew kept at it harder than ever.

The weather began to look squally, and before they had got half through, the wind blew a gale and the rain came down in torrents. This greatly retarded their work. I thought it was impossible for them to work at all with the waves dashing up against the Ship and those huge monsters moving up and down in the water, sometimes so covered that you could scarcely see them. But they worked on and did not cease. There was a complete din of noises on deck—the wind, the rain, the Officers shouting to the Men, the mincing machine, and altogether it was a confused place. One of the stagings gave way and pitched the first Mate into the water, but he did not seem to mind that, but he was up and to work again, wet as he was; in fact they were all as wet as they could well be.

The following day, November 11, the mate escorted Eliza to the blubber room to watch the sailors cut the blubber into small pieces for boiling down in the great

Whalemen of the later brig Daisy
cut in a small whale on deck.

iron cooking pots on deck, called try pots. She did not find the atmosphere pleasant—"The smell of the oil is quite offensive to me"—but it did not seem to bother the men. "I could not refrain from laughter," she writes, "such a comical sight! There the Men were at work up to their waists in blubber. The warm weather had tried [melted] out the oil a good deal and made it soft. I don't see how they could stand in among it, but they were laughing and having a good deal of fun."

Another day passed, with the men still hard at it.

They are as busy as bees, some at one thing and some at another; one Man almost all the time grinding spades, ever since they began to cut in the whales; some are tending the machine and as the pieces come through putting them into the try pots. One Man has a large long handled skimmer, that he skims off the scraps [with], and then he puts them into a large tub that all the time looks full though they feed them on the fire when they want them; as the pots get full they bail it off into a cooler and when it is cold, they put it into casks.

Thus the whales actually cooked themselves with their own leftovers. Finally, stripped at last of their blubber and bone, the great carcasses were set adrift. The crew

had a general time cleaning up. They had to use a good deal of sand to scrub and plenty of water to wash off the decks, and then I think all the grease wont come out the first time, but the deck is yellow pine and it will not soak in so bad. There are a great many casks on deck.

After five hard days and nights, the crew finally enjoyed a well-earned rest. On November 14 Eliza logged, "This is the Sabbath day, and I think that all hands have reason to be thankful that it is and a day of rest."

Yet the work was not quite over; the cooper (barrel-maker) must check out the casks and the men must stow them below.

November 15th—It is pleasant with a fair wind today. A Ship in sight. The men are all busy as they are every day. The Cooper is driving the hoops onto the casks; they are new and shrink and have to be attended to or they will leak. . . . all hands feel pleased. They think they have been quite lucky.

November 16th—Pleasant with a good breeze. The Men are stowing away the oil below. Some are getting their boats in trim, repairing the damaged one and grinding their irons and lances ready to take more whales when they are lucky enough to see them. . . . These whales were taken in Latitude 22,30 South and Longitude 25 West.

Eliza Williams' shipboard world is astonishingly real. Even the more distant scenes are clear—one is on deck peering with her through her glass, watching the tiny figures go through the drama of the chase. But Eliza had no opportunity to see the chase at first hand.

John Whidden, on the other hand, gives an account of a chase during his brief career as a whalerman. In 1848 he had jumped ship in Hawaii at the news of the discovery of gold in California, but failing to get a San

Francisco passage, he signed on the whaler *Samuel Robertson*, out of the *Florida*'s home port, Fairhaven.

Within two weeks they sighted a school of sperm whales:

"There she blows!" came from the lookout stationed at the royal masthead, while to the demand:
"Where away?" came the response:
"Four points off the lee bow, sir!"
Instantly all was excitement. Captain Turner seizing a powerful marine glass, sprang into the rigging, and quickly ascended to the lookout, from whence in a few moments came the order:
"Keep her off four points!"
This was speedily done, and the yards checked in.
There were many hands to do the work, the ship having a crew of thirty-six, exclusive of officers. Shortly we could see from the deck a large school of sperm-whales, heading eastward, swimming slowly along, little anticipating the reception being made ready for them.

On deck, "the whaling gear in each boat was in readiness for lowering," the harpoons and lances were "as bright and sharp as razors," and the line was "as supple as silk." There was a good supply of biscuit should the chase be a long one.

When we were but a short distance from them [the whales], the school sounded. The main topsail was thrown aback, and all made ready for lowering. Though intensely exciting, everything was done very quietly, so as not to alarm the whales. Presently the school broke water about an eighth of a mile astern, and in less than three minutes every boat was in the water, and headed for the whales, while every pound of strength that was in the muscles of the crews was thrown into the oars, until the boats fairly flew through the water.

Just before we reached them, our boat being in the lead, the school again sounded. Lying on our oars, a sharp lookout was kept for their reappearance. In fifteen or twenty minutes they again broke water. No sooner were they sighted than the boats were after them, and shortly the harpooner was ordered to stand up. I could now hear the "choo'o, choo'o, choo'o," as they spouted from their blow-holes.

Fairly quivering with excitement, and turning round to get a good look, I suddenly received a tap alongside the head from the mate at the steering oar, that caused me to see more stars than I ever imagined were made, with a quiet admonition that it was contrary to rules to turn the head to look, when pulling on to a whale.

We were now right between two big whales, at least eighty barrels each. The boat being in whaling parlance, "wood and black skin" i.e. the wood of the boat touching the skin of the whale, by reaching over I could have placed my hand upon one, when the mate shouted to let him have it.

The boat-steerer, who is the harpooner (he changes places with the mate after the whale is struck), became gallied (dazed or frightened) for some unaccountable reason. He was too close for darting, and instead of driving, or setting his iron into him solid, he drove it at him, cutting him down the side, but not fastening securely.

Catching up his second iron, he fairly pitch-paled it over him.

It is a singular fact that, as soon as one whale in a school is struck, all the rest know it. In an instant there was not an earthquake, but a waterquake around us, a seething mass of white water, with heads, flukes, and fins in every direction.

Supposing we were fast, the mate roared, "To stern all!" and all the crew thinking the same, the order was obeyed with a will. In less time than it takes to write it, the whole school, having become gallied, were off to wind'ard, going "fin out," like mad.

When the mate discovered that Fred, the Portuguese boat-steerer, had missed his whale, he was furious, and acted for awhile like an insane man. Catching up a paddle, he threw it at Fred's head, and dashing his hat into the bottom of the boat, jumped up and down upon it, meanwhile cursing him, and the whole boat's crew. Then, starting on another tack, the boat's head was turned, and we were ordered to row to windward after the whales, the mate offering everything he possessed, if we could only overhaul the school. Standing there bareheaded, with one hand on the steering oar, with the other he would set against my oar with a force that almost threw me over the line-tub at each stroke, while the crew pulled as if for their lives. But it was of no avail, and after an hour's hard work the school was about out of sight, and the ship nearly hull down. The boat's head was then pulled round, and, reluctantly, we returned on board, where poor Fred was "broken," and turned forward among the crew. According to his story, he had only been right-whaling, and *was accustomed to a long dart . . . when Fred found himself so close he lost his head.*

In fact, the *Samuel Robertson* caught no whales while Whidden was aboard. Several weeks later, when she put into the Pacific island of Papeete for water and repairs he deserted again. This time he signed on the whaleship *George*, homeward bound after a disheartening voyage of forty-seven months and only 1,200 barrels of oil in her hold.

Such was whalermen's luck—and not at all exceptional. Before the year's end, the *Florida* was to have her own share of discouragement. The beginning had been dazzling: nine whales within the first three months—real "greasy luck." Everyone was excited. "There is nothing else talked about," said Eliza in her journal on December 24. "Some are betting on how much oil these will make and wishing for more before they get to New Zealand."

But the wish was not to be fulfilled. For thousands upon thousands of miles, past Australia and New Zealand, a string of tropical islands, into the icy arctic waters off Siberia, past fellow whaleships by ones and twos and entire fleets, for seven long months the *Florida* did not add a single barrel of oil to her cargo. There were sightings, but luckless ones.

February 28th [1859]. . . . spouts were seen from aloft. Immediately they took their line in and went off. The other boats lowered too in a few moments . . . I thought I hardly ever saw a prettier sight—those five little boats with their blue and white sails on the vast water, the

Whales all around them. But they did not succeed in taking any.

March 4th. A cry of Whales was given from aloft this morning before I was up. It proved to be a Sperm Whale, and it seemed to be the opinion that it was a large one. The Men lowered their boats, but did not succeed in taking him.

April 4th. . . . The Boat Steerer from aloft sang out a spout . . . My Husband lowered for it and fired at it with the Bomb lance gun, but did not hit it. It went down and that was the last we saw of it.

April 28th. . . . Right after dinner there was a Right Whale in sight. The boats were all lowered for him and the first Mate's boat got fast to him. He fired three Bomb lances into him and got near enough to him to cut him with the spade several times, besides the Boat Steerer darting two irons into him. They afterward lost him. One iron proved to be worthless and broke short off. Then the other, after holding him a spell, broke and away he went.

May 31st. . . . Saw a Bowhead [whale] and lowered two boats but could not see him again. Saw some floating ice towards night, some large cakes.

For all such bad luck there were certain compensations to being aboard a whaling vessel. Unlike other Orient-bound ships, the *Florida* was in no hurry. No tea was waiting to be raced back to the high prices of an early market. No ice was dripping profits into the bilge. The

Florida was not a carrier but a hunter, her hold waiting to be filled with oil from a quarry that might be another 1,000 miles away or might rise into view this very moment. So there was no sense of urgency—except in the keen pair of eyes scanning the horizon from aloft—and less impatience with light winds. Whales could come to the ship as readily as the ship to the whales, and thus life aboard was more leisurely than on a merchantman.

Cargo ships only exchanged signals when they passed. Whalers always "spoke" if they could come close enough to another vessel for conversation, and whenever possible a gam—an exchange visit on board for socializing and news swapping—was the order of the day.

Cargo ships were in too much of a hurry to stop off at islands unless there was a critical shortage of food or water, but whalermen made frequent island visits: with voyages lasting two to four years, change was essential to keep life interesting. John Whidden, aboard the *Samuel Robertson*, had been astonished by the number of island visits when "for a fortnight I had all the liberty I wished for. Each day one watch would go on shore, receiving a dollar, as liberty money, while on board, the watch would lay around, doing whatever pleased them."

Eliza Williams took special delight in her island landfalls. Her first stop, a month before the *Florida* caught the five whales, was Brava, capital of the mountainous Cape Verde Islands off the coast of Portugal. It was a favorite whalerman's stop, where fresh fruits, water, and additional crew could be obtained. The large Portuguese population of New Bedford today is a result of the custom of short-handed whaleships filling out crews at these islands.

Eliza was awed by the precipices rising straight out of the sea.

In rowing along beside this Island, it seemed grand and awful to look up at that imence height of rock and mountain, hardly ane vegetation to be seen up those sides, but there was signs of life there in the shape of Goats, Jackasses, and now and then a Cow or two. Those were scarse, but any number of the former all among the crags and shelveing rocks, where I suppose no human foot ever trod. So steep were those sides it seemed as if they went perpendicular up to the top, and the breakers dashing over the rocks at the foot and sounding like distant thunder, it did not seem to me that a human being inhabited that desolate looking Island.

But inhabited it was, and after the customary inspection of the ship by the health officer, Eliza found herself on a jackass, clinging for dear life as it carried her up the heights to the city above. On the way the islanders were as curious about her as she was about them. "They would stop and look at us," she says,

till we were quite by, and laugh and in their language talk as fast, which is Portuguese. I suppose we looked as strange to them as they did to us, dressed so different as we were. They had no bonnets on, but instead had handkerchiefs put on in the form of a turban. The young Women wear very gay ones . . . The Men dress a good deal as they do at home, but the Women nothing like us; they wear very little clothing, just a skirt and a long scarf thrown over their shoulders, pinned behind and hanging down. When they put up their arms you plainly see their chemises, so they have no waist to their dresses.

From the mountaintop Eliza enjoyed looking at the land:

It was pleasant up there and presented quite a picturous view. The Orange, Lemon, Banana, and 2 or 3 other kinds of fruit were growing quite plentiful and were then getting ripe and the trees looked beautiful loaded with fruit. Their gardens were under a high state of cultivation; there sweet potatoes were looking nicely. They [raise] some beans, and with the exception of corn they raise no other grain, so that bread is a luxury to them.

She felt strange staying in the Portuguese governor's big breezy house, but found little familiar things: "The bed is very neat, the toilet table well set off with a china bowl and pitcher, brushes and combs, cologne, hair oil; and everything about the room showed a good deal of taste in the owner. My Husband sat down to write home, while I sought the pillow, tired enough."

The night sounds seemed familiar too—at first: "In the night the crickets made me think of home and I could almost have imagined myself [there], had it not been for the braying of the Jackasses."

The *Florida* left Brava after a stopover of two days, taking along

6 Natives that shipped to go to Sea with us, besides the Men that came in the boat, with my Husband and myself. Then we had some fruit besides other things too numerous to mention. My husband bought a goat so I shall have some milk in my tea and coffee. The things were all got

on board, we had supper, and thus ended that day, leaving Brava far behind.

With Brava barely out of sight, Eliza was already anticipating the next landfall: "I suppose the next land we make will be the group of Islands called Tristan da Cunha; but that will not be for a month or so." But she amused herself watching the variety of fish:

Saw a great quantity of porpoises around the Ship this morning. That seems to be great fun for the Men, trying to catch them, which is not easy they are so spry. . . .

Saw some fish today, called Jumpers. They spout something like a whale, and once in a while they will throw themselves quite out of the water. . . .

We see a plenty of little flying fish about here. They look handsome darting up out of the water, skimming along its surface, and then diveing under again.

The steward and cabin boy caught a bird for her: "He is a beauty and is what they call a Cape Horn Pigeon. He is about the size of a duck, shaped something—the bill and all—like them. He is pure white on the breast and under the wings."

And she looked wistfully through the glass at every passing ship: "One, a large clipper Ship we could see without the glass; the Men, the Captain, also his Wife. She was looking at me, I imagine, anxious with me to see a Woman; she had the glass up to her eyes, I could see. We could almost make out her name, but not quite."

The next important landfall was Mangonui, at the northern tip of New Zealand. Eliza could not have been more casual in mentioning the principal reason for their visit.

It is now about a month since I have written any in my Journal and many things have transpired since then.

The 10th of January we had a gale of wind that lasted till the 12th, the heaviest gale we have had since we left home. On the 11th, the fore sail was carried away. We spoke the Whale Ship Rodman, Capt. Babcock, on the 11th, bound home. Did not exchange many words, it was blowing so hard. They had Pigeons on board and four of them flew on board of us. They are very pretty and my Husband has had a nice house made for them. We have a fine healthy Boy, born on the 12th, five days before we got into Port.

Thus the crew of the *Florida* enjoyed a prolonged stay.

We arrived in the harbor of Monganua on the 17th. I had to stay on board the Ship two weeks. Captain Butler, the Harbor Master, came on board as soon as we were in. He came below to see me, and told me that he would send for his Wife and she very soon came on board to see me and came every day and washed and dressed the Baby. She did everything she could for me, till I was able to go to her house. I had every attention paid me, both on the Ship and at Mrs. Butler's.

The Men, when they went on shore, often brought me Fruit and Flowers, and the Captains of the Ships came on board to see me and brought me something nice. Captain Dehart of the Ship Roman 2nd, came to see me several times, and brought me Oranges, Lemons, several kinds of Preserved Fruits, some Arrowroot, a nice Fan made on one of the Islands that he had stopped at, and a bottle of currant wine.

There were eight Ships in the Harbor when we arrived. One of the Captains—Capt. Charry, of the Ship Harvest —had his Wife with him.

Now it was northward, past many tropical isles, to the Japan Sea. A visit to Hakodate, Japan, where the Japanese officials "were highly pleased with the Baby. They crowded around him, feeling of him, and talking and laughing with him." Still further northward into the icy Okhotsk Sea off the coast of Siberia.

There are great quantities of ice around the land; it is not solid but seems jammed together. It has been brought into the passage by the current and lies right across it. I can see, as we near it, from one point of land to the other. I cannot see how we can get through, but my Husband says he is going through. It is clear water beyond and there are 4 or 5 Ships there. I have been on deck, standing a long time and looking about. It is a rugged country and awfully grand, one bluff after another rising to view, interspersed here and there with a valley; the hills covered with snow; the ice jammed up in large masses in the water; the Ships and all together make it an interesting sight.

The *Florida* managed to push through the ice to join the fleet in the bay beyond, but Eliza was uneasy.

Such large pieces came against the Ship all last night,

"It was such an awful death to die."

it frightened me so that I could not sleep. My husband was up about all night.

We, with some of the other Ships, have sent boats up to the head of the Bay, as far as they can get, to see what the prospects are for whaling up there. We can't get any farther on account of the ice. We don't expect the boats back for 3 or 4 days.

It was a long anxious wait, but the boats finally returned.

June 7th. The wind is still blowing a gale; did not blow quite as hard as this morning. About half past six saw boats through the ice. They seemed to have a hard time getting along. They had to get out on the ice and drag their boats over it. About 8 o'clock I went on deck and they were very near us. I counted 12, but there were 15 in company. We took aboard 5 boats' crews besides our own. We had 10 boats on the cranes at one time. We gave them all their breakfast and in a short time spoke the Ships that they belonged to and they went aboard.

A bitter business, this whaling in arctic waters, but the men took it in their stride. Of one of the lost crews, Eliza learned, "They had to mend their boat with a piece of old canvass; then their provision gave out, and they have been living on mussels for the last three or four days. They were wet, cold and hungry when they found us. . . . They will stay with us till they find their Ship."

Some were not so lucky. A boat crew from another ship were "fast to a Whale, and had their boat stove. The Men got on the bottom of the broken boat, but it was very cold and they one after another got numb with cold and fell off and perished."

Whaling was a dangerous business and there were many ways to die. On August 9, 1859, Eliza was overwhelmed to learn that a black sailor, Tim, aboard the *Florida* had perished.

Tim was gone. It happened this way. They hauled up to the Whale, after making fast to him, to kill him with the lance, and he came up under the boat, tipping it to one side until it filled half full of water. It righted again, but three of the Men out of fear jumped into the water and then immediately turned and caught hold of the boat, capsizing her. The other boat was near and picked up the Men, but poor Tim got foul in the line and went down with the Whale. A short time after, they saw the Whale and got him, and they found poor Tim fast in the line, it being wound two or three times around his arms and once around his body. They buried him in the deep. He was bruised a good deal by being dragged on the bottom. It is a dreadful thing—and to think it happened aboard our Ship! He was the best boatsteerer they had and they all say there is no better to be found. He has taken more Whales for us than any other Man aboard of the Ship, and never missed one. But it is not his services alone that I think of; it was such an awful death to die. He was a colored Man. He was a very pleasant Man. I never went on deck and met him but what he had a smile on his face.

ROLLING HOME

When first I come to New Bed - ford, lads,— I

went up-on a spree. I had mon-ey at last, I

spent it fast, got drunk as drunk could be. And

when me mon-ey it was all gone, 'twas then I want-ed

more, But a man must be blind— to

make up his mind— to go to sea once more.—

(Off to Sea Once More)

227

I slept that night with Angeline,
    the rum had gone to me head.
Me watch was new, me money too;
    in the morning with them she'd fled.
And as I roamed the streets about,
    then every one did roar,
"There goes Jack Rack, poor sailor lad,
    he must go to sea once more."

As I went roaming down the streets
    I met with Rapper Brown.
I asked him for to take me in,
    but he looked at me with a frown.
He says, "Last time you was paid off
    with me you chalked on score.
But I'll give you a chance and I'll take your advance,
    and I'll send you to sea once more."

He shipped me aboard of a whalin' ship
    bound for the arctic seas,
Where the cold winds blow through the frost and snow,
    and Jamaica rum would freeze.
And worst of all, I had no gear,
    for I'd lost all me money ashore.
It was then that I wished that I was dead,
    so I'd go to sea no more.

Some times we was catchin' whales, me lads,
    and sometimes we was catchin' none,
With a twenty-foot oar stuck in our hands
    from four o'clock in the morn,
And when the shades of night come on,
    we'd rest on our weary oars.
It was then that I wished that I was dead
    or sick with the girls ashore.

Come all you fine seafarin' men,
    come listen to my song.
When you come off them long, long trips,
    I'd have you not go wrong.
Take my advice, drink no strong drink,
    don't go roamin' on the shore.
But get married, lads, and have all night in,
    and go to sea no more.

Most men in the forecastle, free of marriage ties, had a fling during the brief shore leave when ships put into port. Every port had its "Paradise Street," where feminine charms lured the sailor to part with his hard-earned wages—and all too often the girls, in league with tavern keepers, persuaded Jack to drink himself into a stupor and rolled him for what little money was left in his pocket. Then, like the lad in the song, he went sorrowfully "off to sea once more."

Waterfront hostelries, ruthlessly organized to take advantage of Jack's loneliness, sent boarding-house runners scurrying on deck with false friendliness and an extravagant welcome. Dana had met them at the end of the *Alert*'s voyage home:

Nothing can exceed the obliging disposition of these runners, and the interest they take in a sailor returned from a long voyage with plenty of money. Two or three of them, at different times, took me by the hand; remembered me perfectly; were quite sure I had boarded with them before I sailed; were delighted to see me back; gave me their cards; had a handcart waiting on the wharf on purpose to take my things up; would lend me a hand to get my chest ashore; bring a bottle of grog on board if we did not haul in immediately—and the like. In fact, we could hardly get clear of them, to go aloft and furl the sails.

This chorus from an old forecastle song said it well:

> He'll lend and spend and not offend
> Until he lies drunk on the ground.
> When the money's gone, it's the same old song,
> "Get up, Jack, John, sit down."

By contrast, Jack found a true paradise when he was on shore leave among the Kanakas, as the Polynesians were called then, in the islands of the Pacific. Dana said of the Kanakas he met on the California coast:

Their customs, and manner of treating one another, show a simple, primitive generosity, which is truly delightful; and which is often a reproach to our own people. Whatever one has, they all have. Money, food, clothes, they share with one another; even to the last piece of tobacco to put in their pipes. I once heard old Mr. Bingham say, with the highest indignation, to a Yankee trader who was trying to persuade him to keep his money to himself—

"No! We no all' same a' you!—Suppose one got money, all got money. You—suppose one got money—lock him up in chest—No good!—Kanaka all 'e same a' one!"

Thus a visit to a Pacific island could be one of the happiest memories of a sailor's life, for the mores and customs of these friendly people were far different from those in the cynical Western ports. Their generosity knew no bounds, and their young women were glad to give comfort to homesick sailors. Second mate Oren B. Higgins of the whaleship *Ann Alexander* noted in his journal on January 29, 1848: "Byrons Island in sight and about forty or fifty canoes alongside with four or five Natives in each one. They left the ship at sundown to paddle their canoes about seven miles to windward. There was some of the Ladies came to be our wives."

Herman Melville, as a sailor aboard the whaleship *Acushnet*, described his landfall in the Marquesas in 1842:

We had approached within a mile and a half perhaps of the foot of the bay when some of the islanders . . . who had managed to scramble aboard . . . directed our attention to a singular commotion in the water ahead . . . At first I imagined it to be produced by a shoal of fish . . . but our savage friends assured us that it was caused by a shoal of "Whinhenies" (Young Girls) . . . coming off shore to welcome us. . . . Some distance from the beach . . . they boarded us at every quarter, many seizing hold of the chain plates and springing into the chains. Others at the peril of being run over . . . catching at the bob stay, and wreathing their slender forms about the ropes, hung suspended in the air. All of them at length succeeded in getting up the ship's sides where they clung dripping with brine and glowing from the bath, their jet black tresses streaming over their shoulders and half enveloping their otherwise naked forms . . .

*A young New England girl's fanciful
rendering of a "marimaid."*

On certain islands the sailor might look forward to news from home. Honolulu was a common port of call for returning merchantmen in search of more cargo to fill out their holds; whaling captains were glad to ship their oil directly from Honolulu to free their own vessels for more hunting. So it was here that in 1852 Sara Smith of Blue Point, New York, addressed her letters to Samuel Smith, her young whalerman son: "I have written a letter and directed it to you at the Sandwich Islean. A man that had been a whaleing told me that was the best way to direct as the whale ships went there Some times for there is Piles of letters there."

Like many mothers' letters, Mrs. Smith's expresses both her own loneliness and her concern for the welfare of her son.

The Power of the allmighty is Sufficient to Preserve you and the Ship and all on Board and it has been my Prayer that it should be so, I feel a hope that we may meet again even in this world and have Pleashure in each others Company. It was a trial to me to have you go to Sea for I was fraid that you might fare hard or be Sick, I knew it would be all new to you, and I thought Perhaps the most of the Crew might be roughf men but then I think there is wickedness enoughf every where, and I belive you Can be Preserved Safe in the midst of it. I am glad that you enjoy yourself on the Sea Since you are there, for I should be verry unhappy if I thought you was and Could not get home for a long time. So my Dear Son take all the Comfort you Can in a good and right way, and I expect to meet with you again when your voyge is over if we should both live untill that time. I suppose whale Ships are off 2 or 3 years. Write to me as offen as you Can and let me know all about things. If you should live to Come back try and bring Some little Curiosity from the Sea with you. Come and See us without fail when the Ship returns if you and me lives. I do not think for a moment but what you love your mother truly.

Even doleful letters like this were a source of comfort to a sailor years away from home. After eleven months with no news, when Richard Dana could hardly contain himself any longer, the *Alert* arrived in California bearing letters from Boston. "These I sat up all the night to read, and put them carefully away to be read and reread again and again at my leisure."

Eliza Williams too, though she had her husband and a child by her side, longed for news. The *Florida* was over eight months out, in the Okhotsk Sea, when Eliza received her first letters from a fellow whaleship, the *South Boston:* "I had not dared hope it was she, I wanted to see her so much, for she was out from home a month later than we, and we expected some news from home."

Nothing sent a greater thrill of excitement through a ship than the order to set sail for home. Dana describes the *Alert*'s eager crew:

All eyes were aft on the captain, who was walking the deck, with, every now and then, a look to windward. He made a sign to the mate, who came forward, took his station deliberately between the knightheads, cast a glance aloft, and called out,

"All hands lay aloft and loose the sails!"

"We were half in the rigging before the order came, and never since we left Boston were the gaskets off the yards and the rigging overhauled, in shorter time.

After battering her way around Cape Horn in the dead of winter, the *Alert* turned her bow northward—a signal to the crew that the captain was not going to take the longer, easterly passage around the Falkland Islands, but head "with her nose straight for Boston, and Cape Horn over her taffrail."

The news ran though the ship . . . It was a moment of enthusiasm. Everyone was on the alert, and even the two sick men turned out to lend a hand at the halyards. The wind was now southwest, and blowing a gale to which a vessel close-hauled could have shown no more than a single close-reefed sail; but as we were going before it, we could carry on. Accordingly, all hands were sent aloft, and a reef shaken out of the topsails, and the reefed foresail set. When we came to masthead the topsail yards, with all hands at the halyards, we struck up "Cheerily, men," with a chorus which might have been heard half way to Staten Island [off Argentina].

Under her increased sail, the ship drove on through the water. Yet she could bear it well; and the captain sung out from the quarter-deck—"Another reef out of that fore-topsail, and give it to her!" Two hands sprung aloft; the frozen reef points and earings were cast adrift, the halyards manned, and the sail gave out her increased canvas to the gale. All hands were kept on deck to watch the effect of the change. It was as much as she could well carry, and with a heavy sea astern, it took two men at the wheel to steer her. She flung the foam from her bows; the spray breaking aft as far as the gangway. She was going at a prodigious rate. Still, everything held. Preventer braces were reeved and hauled taut; tackles got upon the backstays; and each thing done to keep all snug and strong.

The captain walked the deck at a rapid stride, looked aloft at the sails, and then to windward; the mate stood in the gangway, rubbing his hands, and talking aloud to the ship—"Hurrah, old bucket! the Boston girls have got hold of the towrope! . . . Hurrah, you jade, you've got the scent!—you know where you're going!" And when she leaped over the seas, and almost out of the water and trembled to her very keel, the spars and masts snapping and creaking, "There she goes! There she goes—handsomely! As long as she cracks she holds!"

Rolling home! It was the most glorious feeling of all—and a great softener of men. Dana commented on how "the little differences and quarrels which a long voyage breeds on board ship were forgotten, and everyone was friendly; and two men who had been on the eve of a battle half the voyage, were laying out a plan together for a cruise on shore."

A favorite song of all homeward-bound seamen was the classic "Rolling Home," among the few songs sung both below deck as a forecastle song and on deck as a capstan shanty. According to Captain Harry Garfield, one of the last of the sailing masters, "As soon as word was out somebody would break out with 'Rollin' Home' and every man in the watch would join in. The hardest case aboard would 'water up' a bit—even though he might not even have a home to go to."

Indeed, when Lambert Larsen, a retired Swedish sailor serving as the night watchman in Connecticut's Mystic Seaport Museum, was asked if he remembered singing any sea shanties, he got to his feet, seized a yardstick, bent his chest across it—as if for all the world it were a capstan bar—and commenced marching around, singing in his broken English, "Rrrollin' home to dear old Angleland."

Of course, Yankee sailors rolled home to "dear New England."

Captain Thomas Williams.

Rolling Home

Pipe all hands to man the cap - stan, ___ see the
cab - le's free and clear, And we'll heave and heave to
geth - er, ___ for New Eng - land, home we'll steer. Up a
loft and in the rig - ging blows the wild and rush - ing
gale Like a mon - soon in the spring-time, ___ fill - ing
out each well-known sail. Roll - ing home, roll - ing home, roll - ing
home a - cross the sea. Roll - ing home to dear New
Eng - land; ___ roll - ing home, dear land, to thee.

Twice five thousand miles behind us,
    twice five thousand miles before,
Now we're passing St. Helena.
    headed for New England's shore.
And the waves we leave behind us
    seem to murmur as they flow,
"There's a hearty welcome waiting
    in the land to which you go."

CHORUS

So we'll sing a joyful chorus
    through the watches of the night,
Sight the shores of dear New England
    when the gray dawn brings the light.
So heave away and with a will, boys,
    for New England, home we'll steer,
And the girls'll all be waiting
    for us there upon the pier.

CHORUS

But a great change was brewing in the U.S. merchant marine, and had been for many decades. More and more American seamen were rolling home for the last time. The opening of the West and new commercial enterprises offered exciting opportunities and good wages to young men who remained ashore. Many of the fortunes made in shipping were now being invested in railroads and industry. Meanwhile, at sea, wages had not only not gone up, but had actually been reduced—from $15 a month before 1812 to $11 and $12 in the next half-century.

Thus only those Americans dedicated to a career at sea were willing to make the long struggle to the quarterdeck. Others, who could not hold down a shoreside job because of wanderlust or an addiction to the bottle, con-

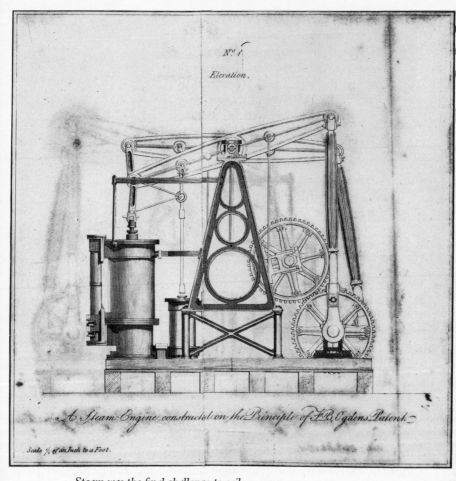

A Steam Engine constructed on the Principle of A. B. Ogden's Patent.

Scale ¼ of an Inch to a Foot.

Steam was the final challenge to sail.

tinued to serve before the mast, but gradually American forecastles became international in flavor. As early as Dana's voyage, three out of four sailors on American ships were foreigners. By the late 1850s when Abbey sailed, the ratio was five or six to one.

By Abbey's time too, one by one the square-riggers themselves were about to roll home for the last time. Speed under sail was no longer the criterion. The clippers were already on the way out, replaced by more lightly sparred ships of greater carrying capacity. Yet even these efficient vessels gradually lost their leadership in world trade.

The die had been cast long before. In 1787 John Fitch had built the first workable steamboat. Robert Fulton's steamer *Clermont* was a commercial success by 1807. In 1814 young Henry Towne, the boy who described his experience with Father Neptune crossing the equator aboard the whaleship *Galatea*, "sailed from Boston to New York by steam ship and there boarded the Galatea, my uncle Solomon Towne, in command." In 1819, assisted by sail, the *Savannah* became the first steamer to cross the Atlantic.

But American shipowners were blind to the *Savannah*'s prophetic voyage; young America was beginning to get her sea legs under sail and was much too preoccupied with attaining supremacy to take much notice of a freak like a steamship. The Black Ball Line had just been established, and within a few years Yankee sailing vessels outclassed England's best. Besides, the argument went, steamers were slow, undependable, dirty, and downright dangerous: they would never amount to a thing.

The British establishment seemed to agree. The *London Civil Engineer and Architects Journal* summarized the attitude by dismissing transatlantic steam travel thus: "The establishment of steam-communication with the moon is quite as feasible—'Earth has its bubbles as the water hath/And this is one of them.'"

Without the steadying influence of sail, early steamships rolled frighteningly in a heavy sea—as Charles Dickens described in his *American Notes:*

It is the third morning. I am awakened out of my sleep by a dismal shriek from my wife, who demands to know whether there's any danger. I rouse myself, and look out of bed. The water-jug is plunging and leaping like a lively dolphin; all the smaller articles are afloat, except my shoes, which are stranded on a carpet-bag, high and dry, like a couple of coal-barges. Suddenly I see them spring into the air, and behold the looking-glass, which is nailed to the wall, sticking fast upon the ceiling. At the same time the door entirely disappears, and a new one is opened in the floor. Then I begin to comprehend that the state-room is standing on its head.

In a more serious vein, Dickens wrote to his biographer, "I observe so many perils peculiar to steamers that I am still undecided whether we shall not return by one of the New-York liners."

But almost every new venture has its dangers, and progress has often been made in the face of public ridicule. Junius Smith, lone American pioneer in transatlantic steam travel, fought an uphill battle to establish the first transatlantic steamship line in 1838. But when the British Cunard Line was created shortly thereafter, supported by a large subsidy from the British government, Smith's line was doomed to failure. Every effort to persuade the American government to grant a similar subsidy was put down by self-seeking private interests, and Britain moved into unchallenged command of ocean steam travel.

Thus, before the first clipper was even built, with her glorious era of sail yet to come, America was already doomed as a merchant marine power. First, merchants had dismissed steam as a fad. Second, with more profits to be made in industry and westward expansion, capital lost interest in sea ventures. Lastly, the U.S. government was not willing to subsidize shipping to help it compete with the subsidized British ships.

The final blow was the Civil War. John Whidden summed up the situation with sorrowful indignation.

Then came the outbreak of our Civil War and as a war measure our tariff was increased on everything pertaining to shipping as well as everything else, which was a deathblow for the time to American ships, the tariff being prohibitory to competition with foreign shipping. Not having a force to protect our merchant marine, the greater part were placed under a foreign flag, mostly English, for protection. Those that remained and still swung "Old Glory" from their peaks, became a prey to Southern privateers—the "Alabama," "Shenandoah," and others . . .

With the close of the war our shipping was reduced to a minimum. Every ship that was placed under the English flag for protection "still remained an Englishman,"

Top left, the windlass of the whaler Charles W. Morgan.
Lower left, sailors stowing away blubber
aboard the whaling brig Daisy. Above, going over
the side in the Daisy's whaleboat.

as they could not again sail the seas under the folds of the "Star Spangled Banner." When they changed their flag, they changed for good.

With the ending of the war all hoped that the tariff, especially on shipping, would be reduced, to enable our shipyards to again resume building, and enter into competition for the world's carrying trade, where we had lost prestige, but it was not to be. The tariff was still kept on, the same as during the war, and no one, under these conditions, was insane enough to build. The carrying trade of the world that should have been in American bottoms was allowed to slip from us, and with it one of our finest New England industries—shipbuilding. . . . American captains who still followed their profession hung on at reduced pay, or went to England, passed the examining board, and obtained command of English ships, sailing them for years. All these considerations combined caused me to make up my mind that I would give up the sea and go into business on shore.

As the age of sail came to its inevitable end, the nation's maritime tradition died with it. Yet for some the dream would never die. Men clung to the canvas backs far into the twentieth century, carrying cargoes for which speed was of little significance—grain from Australia, guano from Chile and Peru, lumber from New England. Despite the discovery of petroleum in 1859, despite terrible losses to Confederate cruisers and in the arctic ice, despite the ever growing competition of steam-driven factory ships of other nations, the whaleships sailed on—until the August day in 1924 when the bark *Wan-*

derer, out of New Bedford, became the last American whaler ever to set sail.

To this day the U.S. Coast Guard Academy maintains a square-rigger, the bark *Eagle*, to give machine-age cadets that feeling of belonging to a ship and the sea itself, a feeling delightfully expressed by a forecastle hand of the *Samuel Russell* in a letter to the New York *Herald*, September 23, 1851.

Hope you will excuse the liberty an unlearned fo'castle salt takes in presuming to pay his services to your honor after this fashion; but d'ye see there's no help for it, seeing as how the beautiful yarn in Saturday's Herald about Yankee pilot boats and Yankee yachts and Yankee steamers, and Yankee clippers, was very awkwardly spun, in one respect, as it seems to me; and that was in neglecting to include among your list of clipper ships, the name of one of the sweetest crafts that ever danced through old Neptune's dominions. I mean the clipper ship Samuel Russell, of this port, built by Westervelt and McKay.

O, sir, you may safely believe it, she is indeed some, and a plain tar begs you will excuse a wholesome jealousy he feels for the reputation of a craft his heart is somewhat bound up in. Why, sir, though nearly every one of the clippers in your long list has been built since the Russell, and of course all supposed to be on Brother Jonathan's scale of gradual improvement, yet I would be glad to stake the wages of a twelve month's voyage, that throughout John Bull's wide extended kingdom, either in his navy or among his merchantmen, no matter what the size of the rig, he has not a vessel among the whole crowd that could successfully compete with the Samuel Russell.

When I made a voyage in that 'ere ship, under command of old Captain Nat Palmer (a captain, let me tell you, as is a captain), we had an experience of so wonderful a character that it has often been a wonderment to me that the ship's owners, or some of her relations, did not blow on it through the newspapers. Scores of vessels on the same tack with ourselves, were overhauled and ran away from with just the same ease as the America beat the Royal yachts of England. Occasionally, to be sure, some brother Yankee would put the good ship to her mettle before we could shake her off; but as to anything foreign—whether English, or French, or Dutch, or what not, and we had chances with all sorts of them—why, Lord bless you, sir, it was the merest baby play in the world.

But lest you consider this only a sailor's yarn, also to give you a more definite idea of her performances on that voyage, allow me to state one fact that may be proved by her log-book. One day, we took a pretty smart breeze upon our starboard quarter, and it continued to blow tolerably steady for the space of ten days. At the end of that time we had skimmed upwards of forty-five degrees, making, as you will perceive, hard onto three thousand two hundred miles in ten days. The handsomest run in any one day was three hundred and twenty eight miles. Now, sir, I humbly submit, if that is not a feat to boast of? If that is not an achievement to entitle a ship to be classed among the clippers? But the most astonishing

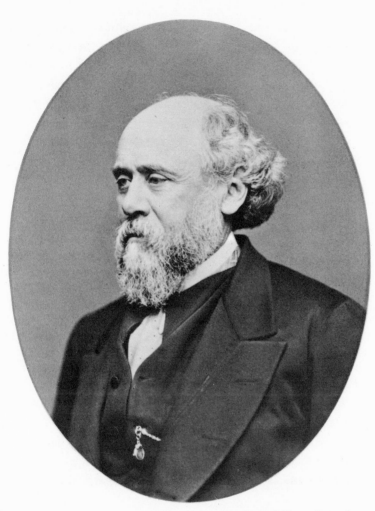

Richard Henry Dana, Jr.,
as an elderly man.

fact of all remains to be told, and I tell it to you on the word of an honest sailor, that, from the time we left Sandy Hook until our return (being the first to report our own arrival in China), I never saw scarce a gallon of water on her deck that did not either come from the clouds or was drawn up by the bucket rope.

I could tell you many interesting facts connected with the history of this favorite ship—how on a subsequent voyage, all hands wrote home from Hong Kong, by a ship that sailed nearly a month before us, and how beautifully we overhauled and passed her, having thereby to deliver the contents of our letters by word of mouth. How—but I must haul in the slack, as your time is too important to be taken up with a rough sailor's yarn. But I will say, however, with your permission, that, in my humble opinion, if the Russell were more heavily sparred, there is not a ship afloat in the world that could outsail her. You may perhaps judge of the correctness of this opinion, when informed that while she is sixty tons larger than the Sea Witch, and is, in all respects fully her equal, yet she carries one fifth less canvas than that justly celebrated clipper.

Hoping that you will excuse this boldness, and that you may shortly herald the arrival of Capt. Limeburner, now in command of the Samuel Russell, I remain your very humble servant,

Robert Steigh
(nicknamed by my messmates "Bob Stay")

GLOSSARY

This glossary, with some additions, comes from Richard Henry Dana, Jr.'s *The Seaman's Friend*.

ABACK The situation of the sails when the wind presses their surfaces against the mast, and tends to force the vessel backward.

ABOUT On the other tack, as in *come about*.

AFT, AFTER Near the stern.

AFTERGUARD The ship's officers.

ALL HANDS The whole crew.

ALOFT Above the deck, in the rigging.

AMIDSHIPS In the center of a vessel, either with reference to her length or her breadth.

ARM, YARDARM The extremity of a yard.

ATHWART Across, at right angles.

AWASH Level with the surface of the water, as when the sea washes over the deck.

BALLAST Heavy material such as iron, lead, or stone, placed in the bottom of the hold to keep a vessel from upsetting.

BARK A three-masted vessel with her foremast and mainmast rigged like a ship's, and her mizzenmast like the mainmast of a schooner, that is, fore-and-aft rigged.

BATTENS Thin strips of wood put around the hatches to hold the tarpaulin down. Or, in Chinese junks, inserted in a sail to keep it flat.

BEAMS Strong pieces of timber stretching across a vessel to support the decks. *On the weather* or *lee beam* is in a direction to windward or leeward, at right angles with the keel.

BEATING Going ahead, even though into the direction of the wind, by alternate tacks.

BEFORE THE MAST To ship before the mast is to ship as a sailor, not as an officer. The term comes from the fact that sailors are quartered in the forecastle, forward of the fore-mast.

BELAY To make a rope fast by turns around a pin or coil, without hitching or seizing it.

BERTH The place where a vessel lies; also, the place in which a man sleeps.

BILGE That part of the floor of a ship on which she would rest if aground, being the part near the keel which is more in a horizontal than a perpendicular line. *Bilgeways* are pieces of timber bolted together and placed under the bilge in launching. *Bilge water* is water that settles in the bilge.

BOATSWAIN *Pronounced bo-s'n;* a seaman not an officer, put in charge of the deck crew when the first mate is on watch.

BOOM A spar used to extend the foot (bottom) of a fore-and-aft sail or studdingsail.

BOW The rounded part of a vessel, forward.

BRACE A rope by which a yard is turned about. To *brace a yard* is to turn it about horizontally. To *brace up* is to lay the yard more fore and aft. To *brace in* is to lay it nearer square.

BRIG   A square-rigged vessel with two masts.

BULWARKS   The woodwork around a vessel above her deck.

BUMBOATS   Boats that lie alongside a vessel in port with provisions and fruit to sell.

BUNT   The middle of a sail. Also, a sail is rolled up into a *bunt* when furled.

CABIN   Where the officers live, aft.

CABLE   Heavy rope fastened to the anchor.

CANVAS   The cloth of which sails are made.

CANVASBACK   A steam sailor's name for a sailing vessel.

CAPSTAN   A device placed perpendicularly in the deck and used for mechanical advantage in heaving or hoisting, especially in weighing anchor.

CAT   The tackle used to hoist the anchor up to the cathead.

CATHEAD   Large timbers projecting from the vessel's side, to which the anchor is raised and secured.

CAULK   To fill the seams of a vessel with oakum.

CHAFING GEAR   Protective padding made from old rope yarn, fastened at places where sails rub against the standing rigging.

CLEW   The lower corner of square sails. To *clew up* is to haul up the clew of a sail.

CLOSE-HAULED   Applied to a vessel with sails trimmed to sail as close to the wind as possible.

COIL   To lay a rope up in a ring with one turn (or fake) over another. A coil is a quantity of rope laid up in this manner.

COME UP   To slack off on a rope or tackle.

COOLIES   Unskilled Oriental laborers. For those working in foreign ports (San Francisco, Cuba, Peru, etc.), this meant virtually slave labor.

CUTTER   A single-masted vessel, similar to a sloop. A *revenue cutter* is a lightly armed governmental vessel used to prevent smuggling and enforce customs regulations.

DAVITS   Pieces of timber or iron, with sheaves or blocks at their ends, projecting over a vessel's sides or stern to hoist boats up to.

DECK   The planked floor of a vessel, resting upon her beams.

DROGHER   A West Indian coasting vessel. The term is usually applied to one-cargo vessels such as hide droghers, lumber droghers, etc.

EVEN KEEL   The situation of a vessel when she is so trimmed that she sits evenly upon the water, neither end being down more than the other.

FAST   A rope by which a vessel is secured to a wharf. To *make fast* is to make secure, or tie.

FIFE RAIL   The rail going around a mast.

FORE   Used to distinguish the forward part of a vessel or things in that direction, as *foremast, fore hatch*; in opposition to aft or after.

FORE AND AFT   Lengthwise with the vessel; in opposition to *athwartships*.

FORECASTLE   That part of the upper deck forward of the foremast; also the forward part of the vessel under the deck where the sailors live.

FOUNDER   A vessel *founders* when she fills with water and sinks.

FULL   Sails filled with wind, not fluttering.

FURL   To roll a sail up snugly on a yard or boom and secure it.

GAFF   A spar that supports the head of a fore-and-aft sail.

GALLEY   The place where cooking is done.

GASKETS Ropes or pieces of plaited stuff used to secure a furled sail to the yard or boom.

GROG Diluted rum.

GUNWALE Pronounced *gun-nel;* the upper rail around the outside of a vessel.

HALYARDS Ropes or tackle used for hoisting and lowering yards, gaffs, and sails.

HAND To *hand* a sail is to furl it. To *bear a hand* is to hurry. To *lend a hand* is to assist.

HANDSPIKE A long wooden bar used for heaving at the windlass.

HATCH, or HATCHWAY An opening in the deck to afford passage up and down. The coverings over these openings are also called hatches.

HAUL The sailor's word for *pull.* To *haul away* means to pull on a rope.

HAWSEHOLE The hole in the bow through which the anchor cable runs.

HEAD Forward part of a vessel; also, the top part of a sail. A *headwind* is an unfavorable wind, blowing from the direction of the desired course. A *masthead* is the upper end of a mast.

HEAVE (HOVE) SHORT To heave in on the cable until the vessel is nearly over her anchor.

HEEL The after part of the keel; also, the lower end of a mast or boom. *To heel* is to lie over on one side.

HELM The devices by which a vessel is steered, including the rudder, tiller, wheel, etc. The term is applied more particularly, perhaps, to the tiller.

HOLD The interior of a vessel where the cargo is put.

HOLYSTONE A large piece of sandstone used for cleaning a ship's decks. A holystoned deck would look whiter.

JIB   A triangular sail set on a stay, forward.

JOLLY BOAT   A small boat, usually hoisted at the stern.

JUNK   Condemned rope, cut up and used for making mats, swabs, oakum, etc.; also, a ship used in Chinese or other waters with square sails spread by battens; also, *salt junk*, meaning salt pork.

JURY   A makeshift used in an emergency, such as *jury-mast* or *jury-rig*. Originally from the French *jour*, "day."

KEEL   The lowest and principal timber of a vessel, running fore and aft.

KNOT   A nautical mile; a mile and a fifth.

LANDFALL   Sighting or reaching land after being at sea.

LARBOARD   The left side of a vessel.

LAY   To come or to go, as *lay aloft, lay forward, lay aft*; also, the direction in which the strands of a rope are twisted, as from left to right or from right to left.

LEE   The side opposite that from which the wind blows. If a ship has the wind on her starboard side, that will be the *weather*, and the larboard will be the *lee* side. A *lee shore* is the shore upon which the wind is blowing.

LIST   The inclination of a vessel to one side, such as a *list* to port or a *list* to starboard.

LOG, or LOGBOOK   A journal kept by the chief officer, in which the situation of the vessel, winds, weather, course, distance, and everything of importance that occurs is noted down.

LONGBOAT   The largest boat on a merchant vessel. When at sea, it is carried between the foremast and mainmast.

LUFF   To put the helm so as to bring the ship up nearer to the wind. *Spring a luff, keep your luff*, etc., are orders to luff. Also, the forward part of a sail.

MARL   To wind or twist a small line or rope around another.

MARLINE Pronounced *mar-lin*; small, two-stranded stuff used for marling, a finer kind of spun yarn.

MAST A spar set upright from the deck to support rigging, yards, and sails.

MIZZENMAST The aftermost mast of a ship. The spanker is sometimes called the mizzen.

MONSOON A seasonal wind in the Indian Ocean and southern Asia, blowing from the southwest in summer and from the northeast in winter.

OAKUM Stuff made by picking rope yarns to pieces and used for caulking and other purposes.

OLD MAN The sailor's name for the captain.

PACKET A ship that maintains a regular route (and often a regular schedule) with specified ports of call, carrying passengers, mail, and freight.

PAWL A short bar of iron that prevents the capstan or windlass from turning back. *To pawl* is to drop a pawl and secure the windlass or capstan.

PAY OFF When a vessel's head falls off from the wind. *To pay out* is to slack up on a cable and let it run out.

PIN A short piece of wood or iron to belay (tie) ropes to.

POINTS Small ropes in the sail for tying up a reef.

POOP A deck raised over the after part of the ship.

PORT Used instead of *larboard*.

PRIVATEER An armed ship that is privately owned and manned, but commissioned by a government to fight or harass enemy shipping.

PROA A small swift Malay sailing boat.

QUARTER-DECK That part of the upper deck that runs aft from the mainmast.

RATLINES Pronounced *rat-lins;* lines running across the shrouds horizontally, like the rungs of a ladder, and used to step on in going aloft.

REEF To reduce the area of a square sail exposed to the wind by taking in on its head—rather like taking a "tuck" at the top.

REEVE To pass the end of a rope through a block.

RIG The cut of a ship, her sail and mast arrangements. *To rig* a ship is to put up her spars and masts, and the rigging required to ready her for sail.

RIGGING The general term for all the ropes of a vessel.

ROYAL A light sail next above a topgallant sail.

ROYAL YARD The yard from which the royal is set, the fourth from the deck.

RUNNING RIGGING Ropes that reeve through blocks and are pulled and hauled, such as braces, halyards, etc.; in opposition to the *standing rigging,* the ends of which are securely seized, such as stays, shrouds, etc.

SAILS They are of two kinds: *square sails,* which hang from yards and are perpendicular to the line of the keel, such as the courses, topsails, etc.; and *fore-and-aft sails,* which are held aloft by gaffs, or on stays, and run parallel to the line of the keel, such as jib, spanker, etc.

SAMPAN A small boat of the Far East, usually propelled by a single scull (oar) over the stern and having a roofing of mats.

SCHOONER A small sailing vessel, usually with only two masts, and having all sails on the lower masts rigged fore-and-aft.

SCOW Any sort of flat-bottomed boat, either rowed or with sail, generally used for short ferrying trips.

SCUD   To drive before a gale with no sail showing, or only enough sail to keep the vessel ahead of the sea; also, low thin clouds that fly swiftly before the wind.

SCUPPERS   Holes cut in the waterways for water to run off the decks.

SEA DOG   An old-time sailor.

SEIZE   To fasten ropes together by turns of small stuff.

SEIZINGS   The fastenings of ropes that are seized together.

SHANGHAI   To kidnap a sailor when he is drunk or doped, and put him aboard an outgoing vessel. Originally the term was used when a ship was going to Shanghai or other Chinese ports. In the early nineteenth century the term for this was *impress*.

SHEET   A rope used in setting a sail to keep the clew down to its place. With square sails the sheets run through each yardarm.

SHELLBACK   An old sailor.

SHIP   A vessel with three masts, with yards and square sails on each.

SHROUDS   A set of ropes, reaching from the mastheads to the vessel's sides, that support the masts.

SKYSAIL   A light sail next above the royal, fifth from deck.

SLACK   The part of a rope or sail that hangs down loose.

SLOOP   A small vessel with one mast.

SPANKER   The after sail of a ship or bark. It is a fore-and-aft sail, set on a boom and gaff.

SPAR   The general term for all masts, yards, booms, gaffs, etc.

SPEAK   To communicate from ship to ship at sea when two vessels pass in sight of each other.

SPUN YARN   A cord formed by twisting together two or three rope yarns.

SQUARE   Yards are *squared* when they are horizontal and at right angles with the keel. Squaring by the lifts makes them horizontal, and by the braces makes them at right angles with the vessel's line.

STANDING RIGGING   That part of a vessel's rigging that is made fast and not hauled on.

STARBOARD   The right side of a vessel.

STAYS   Large ropes used to support masts and leading from the top of some mast down to some other mast, or to some part of the vessel. Those that lead forward are called *fore-and-aft stays,* and those that lead down to the vessel's sides, *backstays.*

STERN   The after end of a vessel.

STUDDINGSAILS   Light sails set on booms outside the square sails. They are only carried with a fair wind and in moderate weather, and are usually called stun'sails.

SUPERCARGO   A business agent for the owner who sails aboard the ship.

SWAB   A mop formed of old rope, used for cleaning and drying decks.

TACK   To bring a ship about, so that from having the wind on one side you have it on the other. A vessel is on the *starboard tack* when she has the wind on her starboard side.

TAFFRAIL   The rail around a ship's stern.

TAR   A liquid gum taken from pine and fir trees and used for caulking. It is put on yarns in rope making, and on standing rigging to protect it from the weather.

TARPAULIN   A piece of canvas covered with tar, used for covering hatches, boats, etc.; also, the name commonly given to a sailor's hat when it is made of tarred or painted cloth.

THROUGH THE CABIN WINDOW An officer who has not first served as a sailor is said to have come in through the cabin window.

TRIM To arrange the sails by the braces with reference to the wind; also, the condition of a vessel with reference to her cargo and ballast. *In ballast trim* is when she has only ballast on board.

TRUCK A circular piece of wood placed at the top of the highest mast on a ship.

TURN To pass a rope once or twice around a pin to keep it fast. *To turn in* or *turn out* are nautical terms for going to rest in a berth or hammock, and getting up from them.

WAKE The track or path a ship leaves behind her in the water.

WATCH The division of time and labor on board a ship.

WATERWAYS Long pieces of timber running along the sides of a vessel and connecting the deck with the sides. The *scuppers* are made through them to let the water off.

WAY The movement of a ship on her course.

WEATHER In the direction from which the wind blows.

WEIGH To lift up, as to weigh an anchor or a mast.

WINCH A mechanical device with a horizontal spindle or shaft and also a wheel or crank. A small one with a wheel is used for making ropes or spun yarn.

WINDLASS The device used in merchant vessels to weigh anchor.

YACHT A vessel of pleasure or state.

YARD A long piece of timber, tapering slightly toward the ends and hung by its center to a mast, to spread the square sails on.

BIBLIOGRAPHY

Museums

One of the best ways to acquire a feeling for the history of America at sea is to go and visit one or another of the maritime museums, where you can actually see and touch for yourself much of what this book has been about. The ship paintings—of clippers, brigs, packets, whalers—are almost always beautiful and handsome. The handiwork of the sailors themselves abounds, whether it be intricate carvings, scrimshaw, painted sea chests, or hand-decorated logbooks. Some of the museums have preserved and restored the old square-rigged vessels: a visitor can walk the decks, get the feel of a rope, or climb down into the forecastle. The listing here is partial, but represents some of the leading maritime museums you can visit.

Bath Marine Museum, Bath, Maine: The fascinating little city of Bath is and has been for generations a major shipbuilding center. The Marine Museum was formerly a sea captain's house. There is a Junior Museum downstairs, and upstairs a good exhibit on Maine's Kennebec-River ice trade as well as a library, paintings, and maritime implements. Nearby is the famous Bath Ironworks, where both merchant and naval ships continue to be built. From Carlton Bridge in Bath you can watch launchings into the Kennebec and see shipbuilding in progress.

Marine Historical Association, Inc., Mystic Seaport, Connecticut: Mystic has been restored as an actual seaport village, where visitors can walk the cobblestone streets and watch what is done in a sparshed, sail and rigging loft, shipping office, or woodcarver's shop. There are several real whaling ships docked at the wharves, among them the wood-hulled *Charles W. Morgan* and the square-rigged training ship *Joseph Conrad*. Inside the museum itself are thousands of ship models, whaling and nautical implements, paintings, prints, and ship figureheads. For school groups too far away to visit, Mystic will mail an exhibit in a sea chest. Admission is $2.50 for adults, fifty cents for children.

Mariner's Museum, Newport News, Virginia: Newport News was and continues to be a major southern harbor. The museum there has collected many fine models of ships and smallcraft, revolutionary relics, and navigational instruments. The collection of large-size figureheads is particularly fine.

Nantucket Whaling Museum, Nantucket, Massachusetts: Opened in 1930, the museum had originally been a "candle-house" where sperm-oil candles were manufactured. Today it preserves whaling implements, portraits, prints, logbooks, and scrimshaw. A merchant's countingroom and captain's office have been specially furnished with relics from Nantucket's whaling days, and you can also visit a shipsmith's shop, whaleboat shop, sail loft, and cooper's shop. The museum is open only during the summer months.

Old Dartmouth Historical Society and Whaling Museum, 18 Johnny Cake Hill, New Bedford, Massachusetts: Here is a fine introduction to the history of whaling. Perhaps the first thing to look for is the 80-foot, half-scale replica of the square-rigged *Lagoda*, which is mentioned briefly in Dana's *Two Years Before the Mast*. You will also want to see the "Panorama of a Whaling Voyage Round the World," a painting that stands 8½ feet high and is more than a quarter of a mile long. Other paintings and artifacts are on display;

there is an especially fine array of scrimshaw. Admission is one dollar.

Peabody Museum of Salem, 161 Essex Street, Salem, Massachusetts: An outgrowth of the East India Marine Society founded in 1799, the Peabody houses some 750 rigged and unrigged ship models, navigating instruments of all kinds, several thousand original oils, watercolors, sketches, portraits, and prints. You can also see scrimshaw, shipboard gear, and tools of the maritime trades; the library frequently displays some of its collection of nearly 800 logbooks and 1200 "clipper cards."

Books*

Of the principal documentary sources used for this book, three are still in print today. Richard Henry Dana, Jr., *Two Years Before the Mast* (several paperback editions) and Harold Williams, ed., *One Whaling Family* (Boston: Houghton Mifflin, 1964) are both worth reading from cover to cover. Not only is Dana's portrayal of life aboard ship unparalleled, but his description of Mexican California is among the best available. In *One Whaling Family*, in addition to Eliza's delightful observations, editor Harold Williams, her grandson, includes further documentary accounts of sea experiences of other Williams' family members, including the disaster of 1871, when thirty-two whaleships were abandoned among the ice floes in the Arctic Ocean. Lucy Larcom, H. B. Parks, ed., *A New England Girlhood* (New York: Corinth Books, paperback, 1961) describes life in a New England coastal town in the 1820s and 1830s with a real feeling for the period.

Otherwise, John D. Whidden's *Ocean Life in the Old Sailing Ship Days* and Charles P. Low's *Some Recollections* are now available only in very large libraries. The diary of

---

* Unless otherwise indicated, the books listed here are in print as of this writing.

Charles Abbey, published in a limited edition as *Before the Mast in the Clippers*, rests in marine libraries and museums. The journal of Henry Towne aboard the *Galatea* and *Doubling the Horn* by Susan E. Brock are both in the G. W. Blunt White Library, Marine Historical Association, Mystic, Connecticut.

The history of the maritime experience of this country is a neglected chapter in our past. Much background can be found in Samuel Eliot Morison, *The Maritime History of Massachusetts 1783–1860* (Boston: Houghton Mifflin hardcover, 1921; Sentry paperback, 1961), which is not only the most authoritative book on the subject, but is beautifully written, lively, and entertaining. For colonial times through the War of 1812, a briefer dramatic history is Robert Carse, *The Seafarers: A History of Maritime America 1620–1820* (New York: Harper & Row, 1964).

The history of ship design has been more fully treated. For the development of the clipper, Carl C. Cutler's magnificent *Greyhounds of the Sea* (Annapolis, Md.: U.S. Naval Institute, 1961) is in a class by itself. Not only does it supply a wealth of statistical information (the measurements, master, place and date of construction, and owner of every fast ship built between 1782 and 1849), but it richly conveys a sense of America's growth as a merchant marine nation. Both the author's prose and the documents he includes make fascinating reading. For ship design overall, the definitive volume is Howard I. Chappelle, *History of American Sailing Ships* (New York: W. W. Norton, 1935). The story of the greatest clipper designer of them all is told in Mary Ellen Chase, *Donald McKay and the Clipper Ships* (Boston: Houghton Mifflin, 1959), a dependable book with particular appeal for young readers.

Because whaling itself is dramatic, its history has attracted much attention. The writings of Herman Melville, part of classic American literature, are also excellent historical documents. *Moby Dick* (several paperback editions) is the finest treatment of whaling that exists. Melville's lesser known *Omoo* (Evanston, Ill.: Northwestern University Press hardcover and paperback, 1967) gives a vivid picture of the Pacific islands, which were frequent whalerman stopoffs. For a firsthand account of one of the bloodiest mutinies ever, there is William Lay and Cyrus M. Hussey, Edouard Stackpole, ed., *Narrative of the Mutiny on Board the Whaleship Globe* (New York: Corinth paperback, 1962). Another documentary account is Francis Allyn Olmsted, *Incidents of a Whaling Voyage to Which Are Added Observations on the Scenery, Manners and Customs, and Missionary Stations, of the Sandwich and Society Islands* (Rutland, Vt.: Charles E. Tuttle, 1969). Olmsted sailed in the 1840s and focuses largely on his ports of call, especially Hawaii.

Turning to secondary sources on whaling, one can find a remarkable array of photographs along with a good discussion of American whaling in Albert C. Church, *Whale Ships and Whaling* (New York: W. W. Norton, 1960). *The Whale* (New York: Simon and Schuster, 1969) is a history of whaling worldwide, full of vivid woodcuts, prints, and paintings, as well as information about whales. Edouard Stackpole, a former curator of Mystic Museum, has contributed *The Charles W. Morgan: The Last Wooden Whaleship* (Des Moines, Iowa: Meredith, Duell, Sloan & Pearce, 1967).

Because our book was concerned with vessels engaged in long ocean voyages, certain aspects of sea life have been omitted, among them the fishing trade. Mary Ellen Chase, *The Fishing Fleets of New England* (Boston: Houghton Mifflin, 1961) is a well presented study of that industry and its history, excellent for young readers.

The two basic sources for a study of the African slave trade are Daniel P. Mannix in collaboration with Malcolm Cowley, *Black Cargoes: A History of the Atlantic Slave Trade* (New York: Viking Press paperback, 1965) and Basil Davidson, *The African Slave Trade*, originally entitled *Black*

Mother (Boston: Atlantic Monthly Press paperback, 1965). Mannix and Cowley deal with aspects of the physical transportation of slaves; Davidson's book is a contribution on the African cultures from which the people were seized. There is an excellent study on the *Wanderer*: Tom H. Wells, *The Slave Ship Wanderer* (Athens, Ga.: University of Georgia Press, 1967).

Songs and Records

For sea songs and shanties, a classic work is Joanna C. Colcord, *Songs of American Sailormen* (New York: Oak Publications paperback, 1964). First published in 1938 under the title *Roll and Go*, it is the accumulation of Miss Colcord's childhood experience aboard her father's vessels. Parenthetically, the same author has written a fascinating sea dictionary, *Sea Language Comes Ashore* (Cambridge, Md.: Cornell Maritime Press, 1945). For whaling songs—and magnificent pictures of scrimshaw and whalermen's logs— there is Gale Huntington, *Songs the Whalemen Sang* (Barre, Mass.: Barre Publishers, 1964).

Several records could be used to supplement this book. Bill Bonyun, *Songs of Yankee Whaling* (American Heritage Heirloom Records) portrays life on a whaleship through songs and dialogue. For a reenactment of a square-rigged vessel getting up anchor and under way, with orders, responses, shanties, and sound effects, there is the Bonyuns' *Roll and Go* (Heirloom Records), available by writing to Wiscasset, Maine 94578. Finally, the high school students of Fieldston, New York, have cut *New England Whaling Through Its Songs and Ballads* (Heirloom Records Ed. 4), available by writing the Fieldston School, Riverdale, New York.

INDEX

ACKNOWLEDGMENTS

As was the case in the making of both our record albums on the sea, Edouard A. Stackpole, then curator at Mystic Seaport, was the first person we turned to for guidance in our search for documentary materials. And, as before, his advice so generously given inspired the start of our project and was a mainstay throughout.

At the Seaport we also wish to thank Dr. Charles R. Schultz, librarian, Mrs. Anor Van Winkle, assistant librarian, and Donald Judge, in charge of manuscripts, for helping us to take our first steps there in the G.W. Blunt Library.

We gratefully remember the warm welcome and kind help given us by Paul Oliver Blanchette and Lydia Goehmann Andrews, librarian and assistant librarian, at the Peabody Museum of Salem, where we were able to get a real feel of the days of the China trade.

And here at home, at the Bath Marine Museum, we shall always be grateful to the curator, Harold Brown, and to Nancy Brown, librarian, for their cheerful patience and unending willingness to lend books and answer questions.

We also wish to thank Dr. Edward S. Smith for the use of letters from his great-grandmother, Sara Smith, to her son in the South Seas. Mr. Philip F. Purrington of the Whaling Museum, Old Dartmouth Historical Society, helped prepare *the map of the Florida's voyage, and offered kind assistance in the gathering of pictures.*

At Knopf we had four editors to turn to, and to each go special thanks: to good friend and series-editor "Tony" Scott for his overall concept of the book and continued guidance toward its objectives; to Fabio Coen, executive editor, for his steadfast support of our basic style and approach; to former editor Mrs. Edite Kroll for her enthusiastic response to our first efforts; and to Judy Engelhardt for her never-ending patience and encouragement, her material contribution in editing, and her endurance of Maine winter cold, all of which have made her truly part of this book.

Grateful acknowledgment is made for the use of illustrations:

Bostonian Society, 161; Fogg Art Museum, Harvard University, 249; Harold Williams, 237; Historical Society of York County, Pa., 118; *Lever's Young Sea Officer's Sheet Anchor,* 62; Mariners Museum, Newport News, Va., 178; Metropolitan Museum of Art, *frontis,* 20, 126, 185; Museum of Natural History, 58, 210, 244 bottom, 245; National Gallery of Art, Index of American Design, 171; National Maritime Museum, Greenwich, England, 192; New-York Historical Society, 92, 148, 161; New York Public Library, manuscripts, 140, 167, prints, 33, rare books, 240; New York Society Library, 35, 40; New York State Historical Association, 96, 101, 224, 232; Peabody Museum, Salem, Mass., *jacket,* 24, 55, 87, 135, 145; Whaling Museum, New Bedford, Mass., 7, 72, 89, 106, 206, 244 top. The maps in this book are by John Bierhorst.

BILL and GENE BONYUN have turned what was once a hobby—folksinging—into a profession. For some years Bill, a graduate of Columbia University Teachers' College, had been teaching fifth grade, while Gene worked for a newspaper. Lovers of music—Bill plays the guitar, Gene the cello—they began to experiment with conveying history through song. In 1955 they set up a music folklore department for Old Sturbridge Village, Massachusetts, and soon were making records for the classroom. Albums on their own Heirloom label now include *Yankee Legend, The American Revolution Through Its Songs and Ballads,* and *The Civil War Through Its Songs and Ballads*—the last a winner of a Freedoms Foundation award.

The Bonyuns, who have three sons, now live in a farmhouse on an island in Maine. "Within sight and smell of the sea," they regularly travel up and down the east coast singing history in school classes.

JOHN ANTHONY SCOTT has taught at Columbia and Amherst colleges, and since 1951 has been Chairman of the Department of History at the Fieldston School, New York. He is currently a Professor of Legal History at Rutgers University. Among the books he has authored or edited are *The Ballad of America* and *The Diary of the American Revolution.*

Text set in Electra
Composed by Brown Bros. Linotypers, New York City
Printed by Halliday Lithograph Corp., West Hanover, Mass.
Bound by The Book Press, Brattleboro, Vt.
Typography by Atha Tehon